# Math Word Problems for Smart Kids

Keep your Child Trained with Intriguing Math Problems

Brendon Stock

electronic means or in printed format. Recording of this publication is strictly prohibited and any storage of this document is not allowed unless with written permission from the publisher. All rights reserved.

The information provided herein is stated to be truthful and consistent, in that any liability, in terms of inattention or otherwise, by any usage or abuse of any policies, processes, or directions contained within is the solitary and utter responsibility of the recipient reader. Under no circumstances will any legal responsibility or blame be held against the publisher for any reparation, damages, or monetary loss due to the information herein, either directly or indirectly.

Respective authors own all copyrights not held by the publisher.

The information herein is offered for informational purposes solely, and is universal as so. The presentation of the information is without contract or any type of guarantee assurance.

The trademarks that are used are without any consent, and the publication of the trademark is without permission or backing by the trademark owner. All trademarks and brands within this book are for clarifying purposes only and are the owned by the owners themselves, not affiliated with this document.

# INTRODUCTION

Kids begin to practice and solve maths word problems in elementary school. Learning how to do word problems teaches your child to apply math to solve problems in everyday life. But many students, even at the college level, are intimidated by simple word problems. The trick is to pull the right numbers out of the problem and use the written clues to set up a mathematical equation.

A problem solver is one who questions, explores, and investigates solutions to problems; show the ability to stick with a problem in order to find a solution; understands that there may be several ways to arrive at an answer; considers many different answers to a problem, applies mathematics to everyday situations and uses it successfully. You can encourage your children to be a good problem solver by involving him or her in family decision-making using math.

To communicate mathematically means to use numbers, words, or mathematical symbols to explain situations; to talk about how you derive your answer; to listen to others' ways of thinking and maybe alter their thinking; to use pictures to explain a situation; and to write about mathematics, not just give an answer. You can help your children learn to communicate mathematically by asking them to explain a mathematical problem or answer. Ask your them to write about the process she or he used or draw a picture of how they derived an answer to a problem.

Reasoning ability means thinking logically, seeing similarities and differences about things, making choices based on those differences, and thinking about relationships among things. You can encourage your child to explain their answers to easy math problems and the more complicated ones. As you listen, you'll hear your child sharing her reasoning.

Important Things To Know

1. Problems Can Be Solved in Several Ways While some math problems may have only one solution, there may be many methods to get the right answer. Learning math is not only finding the right answer; it is also a process of solving several problems and applying what you have learned to new problems.

2. Wrong Answers Can Help! While accuracy is significant, a wrong answer could help you and your kid discover what your he or she may not understand. The incorrect answer tells you to look further, ask questions, and see what the incorrect answer is saying about the kid's understanding. It is likely that when you studied mathematics, you were expected to solve lots of problems using one memorized technique and to do them quickly. The focus now is less on the quantity of memorized methods and memorized problems and more on comprehending the concepts and applying thinking skills to derive your answer.

Sometimes, a child may arrive at the incorrect answer to a problem because they misunderstand the question being asked. For instance, when kids see the problem 5+____ = 8, they respond with an answer of 13. This is because they think the problem is asking, "What is 5+8?" instead of "5 plus what missing number equals 8?"

Ask your child to explain how a mathematical problem was solved. The explanation might help you discover if your kid needs help with the procedures, the number of skills, such as subtraction, multiplication, addition, and division, or the concepts involved. In working with your children, you may learn something the teacher might find very helpful. A call or short note will alert the teacher to possible ways of helping your child learn math more easily.

Help your children be risk-takers. Help them see the value of attempting a problem even if it is challenging for them. Give your children time to explore the different methods to solving a problem. Your child's method might be different from yours, but if the answer is correct and the method of solving it has worked, it may be a great alternative. By encouraging kids to talk about what they are thinking, we help them have stronger math skills and become independent thinkers.

3. Doing Math in Your Head Is Important

Have you noticed that very few people take their paper and pencil out to solve problems in the restaurant, department store, grocery store, or in the office? Instead, most people estimate in their heads or use calculators or computers.

Using calculators and computers demands that people put in the correct information and know if they are reasonable. Normally, people look at the answer to determine if it makes sense, applying the mathematics in their heads (mental math) to the problem. This, then, is why mental math is so important to our children as they enter the 21st century. Using mental math can make children stronger in everyday math skills.

4. It is Okay to Use a Calculator

It is okay to use computers and calculators to solve math problems. Students are taught to use calculators at a young age and are often required to do homework and take tests. The Scholastic Assessment Test (SAT), for instance, permits the use of calculators for its timed tests. Many schools teach computer courses that include using spreadsheets, statistical displays, and computer-assisted designs for graphics and mechanical drawing. Schools often sell calculators to families at a low cost or supply them for all students to use. Knowing how to use a computer, calculator, or an Ipad is a benefit for all students.

# CHAPTER 1: USEFUL STEPS IN MATH TO SOLVE WORD PROBLEMS

Once the children have learned the nature of numbers, word problems will generally be given to them to test how well they have absorbed the lessons. Initially, most kids will find it a challenge. Not only should they have to compete with numbers. Rather, they have everything they know to merge. Their reading and comprehension skills will be tested. They would have to make use of their talents in analytics and cognition. To top it off, they need to make sure they have achieved a detailed knowledge of multiple math application numbers.

But the good news is, there's no reason for them to be burdened. We also narrowed down a list of 4 effective measures to train the children to assist them with their word issues.

4 Measures for Math Word Problems

1. Comprehend the question.

The most important aspect is this. Children ought to consider what the math dilemma applies to. By stating the topic differently, you will support your children. Using different items for which he or she is acquainted. When they can relate to the subject, they will be able to get a deeper understanding. For your kid to get lost in a sea of so many words is a normal propensity. It would be best if you attempted to split the issue into simplified pieces. When the first part of the topic is grasped, they will proceed to the next part. They will know, this way, what the dilemma as a whole is about.

2. Choose the most effective plan for you.

How do they respond to the right approach? In heuristic math, you can try different approaches. Is it the visual image, the measured estimate, the phase going through, or the issue's restatement? Although, in the first phase of understanding the dilemma, that last bit is most fitting. The solution is selected based on the child's desired preference and the issue's need.

3. Solve the situation.

Go on to test it out for the dilemma after you've picked the solution. See how it's appropriate and how well your kids use it. But to be able to make use of it, your kid needs to know the technique entirely. In our earlier blogs, you can review the thorough explanation of each strategy.

4. Go over the solution.

Had he got it, right? Are there any redundant measures? What has to be done to eliminate these redundancies? Is this the solution here? Should he take another approach? Will it have been better?

These are just some of the questions you need to worry about to strengthen your child's intellectual ability and ensure that he knows what to do with the successful term's problems.

Example

Question: The basket has only tomatoes and mangoes. In all, there are 50 things, and 15 are tomatoes. How many mangoes do they have?

Comprehend the question. Break the issue down into smaller pieces. What are the kinds of things in the basket? Mangoes and onions. How many were the tomatoes? Fifteen. How many things, in particular, are there? 50. 50. What are you in need of? The number of mangoes.

Choose the most effective plan for you. Here, you can use the procedure to go through it. For 15 red-colored sticks, get 50 sticks. Then, count how many bright non-red sticks there are.

Resolve the problem. Do the algebra. Just count, and you can get 35 or easily deduct 15 from 50.

Go over the solution. Is this the right solution to fix the issue? In this instance, it is.

Helping Math Loving Your Kid

It is very popular to hear parents complain about their child's school's success, especially in maths. For this cause, both the public and private sectors have developed a lot of specialist learning institutions. Various learning institutions, such as private tutorials and workshop centers, are much more focused on making children understand the topic and, most importantly, overcome any future dissatisfaction with the topic.

While parents struggle to find successful teaching methods, since they are humiliated, upset, and discouraged, children are also starting to lose their interest in the subject. Then they grow the mentality of "I hate Math."

If your kid hates math or has problems with it, what do you do?

Instead of fretting or moaning about your child (which would lead to the sadness of your child), educators claim that helping him or her resolve frustrations or disappointments is the safest way to be effective.

Find a good starting point. Reputable math learning centers typically have a diagnostic test to find the most suitable learning methods for your infant. Your child's carefully selected materials will also help create trust and improve self-esteem. Cool children's math methods are perfect ways to help kids cultivate a good approach to math and other topics.

Here are several approaches used by math learning centers that you can find helpful at home for your child:

Written System. It would be best to allow your child to do written practice by drills and worksheets to achieve a foundation for the orderly growth of mathematical reasoning and talents since it is an important part of mathematics education.

A technique in graphics. This approach makes it important for problem-solving. To illustrate ideas and principles, use photographs, maps, and tables. To give your child insights into problems and overcome the written language, you will find picture-based workbooks.

Mental process. Teach your child how to use mental math strategies and when to do so. For instance, telling them to think 10 + 10 + 10=30-3=27 to higher numbers while adding 9 + 9 + 9.

Verbal process. This is very beneficial, particularly when language is more interesting for your kid. In the sense of mathematics, show your child the meaning of root words. You can also show him or her how to explain her thinking process and logic orally. For example, by breaking down the term into "per CENT" and meaning "for each 100," you teach percentage. 5 percent of 200 will make her or him consider 5 for the first 100 and 5 for the second 100 for this concept. Consequently, 5 + 5 = 10.

The technique of Tactile. If your kid likes to play with cards, dice, chips, and other manipulations, he or she would certainly be involved in this strategy. To teach your child the fundamentals of math, you can use all kinds of coercive approaches.

The four key mathematical operations are best for learning to count chips: addition, subtraction, multiplication, and division. Dice and cards are the most suitable approach for studying chance.

Problems of Math Words and problematic words

New research by Cecilia Kilhamn of the University of Gothenburg shows that word problems and metaphors muddle our statistics. Several students were asked in one experiment to solve equations based on direct instruction and symbolic interpretations. Researchers discovered that all of these descriptions caused students to over-think questions and wrongly set up issues, with many of the difficulties circling the notion of positive and negative numbers. In certain cases, students stopped using negative numbers to set up calculations and sought to modify the problems to work instead for positive integers.

Kilham suggests that this is not a mere error on the respondent's part, but a "reluctance to consider negative numbers." She also states that this is "similar to our need to be able to concretize what is abstract and comprehend negative numbers in terms of concepts such as loans, lifts or temperatures." However, all of these "concepts" are difficult to express to students who do not have co-conceptions.

In the way we describe mathematical ideas, Kilham implies a transition. Students can better understand the core ideas required to tackle word problems later by concentrating on numbers at an early age. The research also shows that students' understanding of symbology, such as decimals or fractions, grows quicker than their interpretation of, say, a pie cut in half to reflect 1/2. Furthermore, the usage of metaphors can create problems with diversifying student perception and cultural differences. This is not to suggest that learners in real life can stop understanding the consequences of statistics. The study by Kilhamn agrees that when children learn their basic math skills, they can begin with traditional symbology and gravitate to correlative experiences later; only then will they fully integrate these ideas into their everyday lives.

For students, this poses a particular challenge. How do we concentrate and still make math fun on this collection of fundamental symbology? Without distracting students from the challenges at hand, iteration and game-driven math calculations will help develop logical ability. These concrete values outside of the school will be further reaffirmed by outside education and math tutoring. Math tutors should cater to students' collection of interactions and change their method accordingly as students find those problems difficult. We believe in the chance to build an adaptive learning experience here at Five Points Learning to solve the confusions that occur in the classroom. Vague terms and metaphors, perhaps, are not the main cause of misunderstanding. Instead, it will make a big difference in the way students retain knowledge when using these devices to explain issues. Each child has its way of interpreting the curriculum, after all, and it is up to us to channel and nurture this learning capacity.

# CHAPTER 2: SIX TIPS FOR TEACHING KIDS TO SOLVE WORD PROBLEMS IN MATH

For many children, math word problems are difficult and often looked at as drudgery that children dread in mathematics class. Word problems are challenging for children because they mix math with literacy, and special thinking skills are required to break down a word problem to solve it.

Let us take some of the pain and stress out of solving word problems by exploring some methods for making this difficult but necessary mathematical task easier to solve.

### Find Key Phrases in Word Problems

To start, parents and kids alike need to comprehend what the word problem is asking. The first step to do this is to look for common words often used in word problems. Certain keywords and phrases shows the type of operation to be used in the problem.

To help your children further, create flashcards or a chart of commonly used words by an operation. On the flashcards or a chart, break up the keywords by operation: subtraction, multiplication, addition, and division.

## Add or Subtract, Multiply or Divide?

As mentioned above, be on the watch out for words that indicate which operation should solve the problem. Certain phrases and words, like "sum," "all together," "total," or "both" indicate that the problem is an additional problem. Other words, like "percent or "half," tell students to use division.

After creating a flashcards or chart, help your child with the problem at hand. Read the problem and look for the words to determine which operation your kid should use to solve that problem.

## Identify the Type of Word Problem

This is the next step. Determine what type of word problem is right in front of your child. This differs from the operation used to solve the problem. Word problems come in 4 main types:

- Part-part-whole problems
- Join problems
- Compare and Seperate problems

All of these word problem types have their unique sub-types. Certain types, like joint problems, are normally used as addition problems. With loads of information, tips and tricks online to master each type, study the different categories to help your child differentiate between problems.

**Break Down Math Problem**

Problems are easier solved when they are broken up into small, manageable parts. One way to do this is to differentiate between the facts given in the problem and the facts. Help your child identify what facts are known before trying to solve a word problem. Also, ensure your child knows what each word in the problem means and define any word as necessary.

## Visualize Elements of the Problem

Many kids are visual learners and can solve a tricky problem when they can see it laid out before them. For this technique, simply help your child draw out the items and amounts listed in the problems. They can draw pictures described in the problem itself or use counters or dots to serve as a visual while they work.

After practicing math word problems using pictures often, students will eventually train their brains to visualize the problem's facts in their heads. As children grow older and gain the necessary cognitive skills and practice, they will quickly visualize parts of word problems in their minds without the need for paper.

# CHAPTER 3: WHY MATH GAMES FOR KIDS ARE A GOOD IDEA

---

Math is not something that you are born to know; it is a talent you practice and need to build. Children who have math issues may become discouraged and feel dumb or decide that they're only something they're not 'great at.' For someone to ignore, math is too big a part of daily life. They are more likely to invest in the subject if you teach kids that math is something approachable, a realistic skill, and something fun to practice. For parents and teachers, which is why math games for children are such an opportunity.

Kids' math games will get your son or daughter involved in math at a young age and promote and enhance a mathematics base as she or he grows.

It's important to illustrate that math doesn't have to be daunting. Using math games for children, you can introduce the topic at an early age. As soon as your child begins to interact with the world around him or her, you will begin playing counting games. They try to sort the world out when children are young, even as infants. A great quality to foster is this inherent curiosity about everything. When they grow up and go to school and life, it will support them. What drives learning is enthusiasm.

Children's math games will introduce children to problem-solving, quick equations, reasoning, interpretation, and much more. At an early age, learning the core mathematics concepts will support them as they begin to study the advanced principles as they grow up.

You should explain how math is used in daily activities to your son or daughter or students.

Learning to say time teaches the sequencing, addition, and subtraction of numbers and measurements.

Counting coins is a good way to exercise the rules of universal mathematics such as addition, subtraction, division, and multiplication, as well as percentages and meaning.

A fun and imaginative way for younger children to learn about numerical values are to use cue cards with numbers and images.

Use stories, rather than just "doing the math," to introduce problems.

Children's math games are a fun way to build a foundation for lifelong interest and math success. It's never too late to start, and there are plenty of games for older children, including video games, that can help understand more complex math types and create that much-needed trust factor!

Top Kids' Android Apps

The era of cell phone users is getting younger and younger. You've noticed your child finding his or her way to your phone, I'm sure. The buttons, the colorful screen, and the fun graphics all make little imaginations very inviting. To the equation, add toddler-focused applications, and they are glued! Fortunately, with several games that not only teach your child and are safe but keep them entertained, developers are right there with you! These five apps will keep kids quiet and amused at any age.

1) ABC Children-James N Numbers and Shapes ($1.00)

Your child will learn letters, numbers, and shapes while playing this game by seeing images and words. Music increases the feeling each time they hit one of the letters, numbers, or shapes. Other game models, including berries, food, livestock, cars, or SpongeBob, can also be downloaded.

2) Toddler Lock-( Free) Marco Nelissen

The greatest of its sort is this toy/phone lock feature. Your kid will hear songs, see shapes and colors, and all the time, and your phone is safe from unintended phone calls or unintentional app releases. There is even an alternative to placing the phone in airplane mode to keep your child safe from radiation.

3) Math Workout Lite-( Free) Workout Games

Math & Workout doesn't sound fun in that same sentence, does it? These math games enable both you and your children to learn and to keep their abilities at their best. Games include I'm Feeling Clever, The Brain Cruncher, Online World Challenge, Math Blaster Challenge, Addition and Subtraction, Multiplication, and Division.

4) Puzzle of Kids Madagascar-Playgamesite.com (Free)

What child is not in love with the Madagascar film? Your children will be happy for hours with this puzzle game, placing the pieces of a Madagascar themed puzzle in the right order.

## 5) Flashcards for Kids-Mo'Blast ($1.99)

By reading, hearing, and spelling the words and images seen on a flashcard-style image, your child will be entertained and learning simultaneously. For each on-the-go parent, audio and automation make this software a must-have.

## Benefits of children's improvised math learning experiences

It can become fascinating and meaningful for kids (preschoolers) to use bright and enjoyable resources while teaching Math. This can also go beyond the number counting. Patterns, sorting and sets, number identification, forms, comparisons, measurements, time, income, addition, and subtraction are other math principles. The thing about mathematics is that it may not be easy, but knowing and enjoying it is impossible. Your child will achieve more than an awareness of the sometimes overlooked topic with a math tutorial center's help and direction.

Kids use these ideas during the day and practice math in ways that are natural for them. They are introduced to forms simply by playing with tiles. If they tell you that the big hand is on the 12th, and so it's lunchtime, they say time. Most of what preschoolers understand in mathematics comes not from dittos and worksheets but from things they want to do. Any of the advantages of making the children experience a specialized math learning activity are given below.

1. Focus and dedication.

The bulk of kids will have math issues. A watchful teacher may often find it tough, but most commonly, this is not necessarily the case; most teachers may not have enough time to commit to only one pupil.

2. Strong learning foundation.

Your kid will develop a substantive basis for the subject with the right math tutors, from the earliest to the best. Without challenge, even though the ideas and topics grow more complicated, he will go up a step.

3. Opportunity to excel.

Improvised activities for math learning are not just for children who are struggling with the subject. For children who do well with it, it may even be of great value. You provide him with the chance to progress his learning by getting your kid into a math lesson center. To get into a good university or to take up a mathematical career, he will use this.

4. Develop better study habits.

For that matter, math tutors, or any tutor for any subject, will provide more productive research techniques for your boy. The approaches will mimic the learning pattern of your kids. And the methods can be adapted by your child to other topics.

5. Learn to be productive at school.

Your kid could do better with curriculum-based after-school programs instead of going home, jumping on the phone, or playing video games. As a mom, you will not only feel comfortable knowing that after school, your child is active, but you will also feel happier having invested in the potential of your child.

Educational Activities for Kids

For girls, there are several different online educational experiences. Their curiosity is expected to peak in using the system as they grow older and see their parents on the screen. As grown-ups do, they would want to get there and play football. You should select fun opportunities so that the time spent on entertainment without the kids understanding it would also encourage learning. Further details about how you can make studying enjoyable with only your machine are as follows.

As a mom, you can find educational games and events for kids of all ages on the Internet. You will also find different games linked to the subject. Some websites provide interesting stuff for kids to work with principles like addition, subtraction, multiplication, and more if you're looking for math. Reading is also appreciated online by taking part in enjoyable games. Although they follow along with the words on the page, some places read stories to children.

Several educational programs for children online are also provided by science and social studies. Between these two school subjects, several common topics can be turned into enjoyable learning activities. You will find activities concerning the life cycle, the solar system, and photosynthesis for research. The social sciences topic deals with the memorization of history. By enjoying fun Internet games, children can learn more about leaders, conflicts, and other nations.

For these educational programs, you might want to set aside a certain time for your kids to access the Internet. Some prefer to leave their kids on screen 1 to 2 days during the week for an hour. On weekends where there is little to do than in the evenings, other parents may reserve the right to screen time. Make sure you're there to answer questions, connect with your kids and their sports, and keep them on the right websites.

Build a list of websites that you have noticed that offer enjoyable experiences that provide the chance to learn while being entertained. You may give your child the option of learning about spelling, reading, or some other topic with this collection. It is smart to work further on any issues that your child is dealing with within education. Making fun will make it easier for your child to understand the subject. When engaged in a fun task, this might help them get a higher score.

If you can see, to make studying enjoyable, all you need is a computer and an Internet connection. There are interactive activities for children that can be found on just about any subject imaginable worldwide. Ensure that you know what your kids are doing on the Internet, and feel free to play now and then in their sports.

Reasons to use kids' math games.

Children's math games are undoubtedly a success. Parents like the idea because it encourages their kids to participate in the topic and improve math skills at a young age. Teachers often use children's mathematics activities to get exposed to new subjects or skillsets for instruction.

Here are the top 5 reasons why you should use kid's math games:

1. In a fun and immersive manner, mathematics games introduce the subject and various math styles to youngsters, making it less challenging.

2. Critical thought, analytics, and problem-solving, as well as the mathematical fundamentals of addition, subtraction, division, and multiplication, are facilitated by math gamers.

3. Math games illustrate the importance of math and teach children that they are using math in ways they have never dreamed of. For a failing pupil, this will create faith in their mathematical abilities and make all the difference.

4. Working as a community may include math games. It teaches children about communication,

cooperation, and helping each other against a shared purpose.

5. Games in mathematics will include students in a way that simple math lessons do not. They can provide meaning for the topic and divide concepts into tangible examples. The strategy will also be required for sports, making the players more involved than just doing worksheets.

Children's math games should not have to be costly. In reality, they are usually a steal compared to a private math teacher for the number of times kids will spend. However, they can be imaginative and inspire kids, which seems to be more complicated with the free-range. There are several ways in which math games can keep children involved and interested in the subject, whether they are dominos, Sudoku, Collection, or a stock market scenario. Although studying, nothing beats having fun! For the critical preparation activity, this is much more important because, as the saying goes, it is a practice that makes it better!

How to Incorporate Math Beyond Multiplication

It can be hard for your child to understand when it comes to learning math, especially when you get into more complex things like fractions, exponents, and decimals.

What will 6.3 x 2.8 be? Know this from the top of your head? It can be frustrating for most adults, but with an active interest in your child's way of thought, it can be made simpler. Fundamental Arithmetic must go deeper than multiplication.

Why are people so scared of math? Simply put, because it's like something new to understand. It's frightening that most word problems are monotonous and do not relate to the real world's circumstances. (Does it matter to you where trains meet?)

So, the first thing you can do is adapt it to circumstances in the real world. If you have a house where people frequently play Texas Hold'em Poker, buy many poker chips and make it look like your child is playing the game.

Bring out the chips and say, "Okay, here you have 132 chips. Make them into piles of 11 and tell me how many piles you have" if your child is learning division. Exponents such as multiplication can be treated, and fractions and reciprocals can be integrated equally.

What should be done? Math can be a lot of fun, so you've got to integrate it into something your child loves. If your kid likes music, get something with a lot of songs in it for that kid. Give them an opportunity by giving them a prize for doing better by creating sports games that use math if your kid is interested in sports. It's better than it sounds to you.

In conclusion, the child's level of motivation in math can be a big influence on their grade level, making learning enjoyable for them. It will be easy to get simple arithmetic into multiplication if it's fun for the child to learn.

Using Worksheets for Math

I believe in the importance of mathematics in our everyday lives, and with proper math education, we need to nurture our kids. Mathematics contains patterns and structure; reasoning and estimation are all of it. In understanding science and technology, understanding of these math principles is also needed. For most girls, learning math is very challenging. It leads parents to feel depression and anxiety. How much tension do our children endure?

The meaning of math, as well as all the advantages, is known to parents and students. Given how important math is, parents will do whatever it takes to help their troubled kids handle math anxiety effectively. You will play a big role in helping the children deal with these difficult items by using worksheets. This is a fun way to teach our kids that it can help them develop by practicing their math ability. Here are some of the benefits of using worksheets and algebra.

Practice makes perfect.

To memorize principles and solutions, learning math involves practice. Studying with math worksheets will give them a chance; by giving them regular practice, math worksheets will improve their math skills. Working with this instrument and answering worksheet questions increases their capacity to reflect on their vulnerable areas. Math worksheets give the children the chance to use problem-solving skills by the practice tests simulated by these math worksheets.

Nice and attractive

Worksheets can be created using colorful graphics using modern word processing applications and devices, which children can find appealing. This makes them more calm and comfortable; the worksheet can look more like a test than a game. Children will feel excited to learn by using this colorful format. Now they are creating online worksheets that have animated graphics, the most exciting component. From wherever they have internet access, they can be viewed on a website, making it an enticing solution to amuse your child while studying.

Record Trail

Another value of these math worksheets is that children and parents can be retained to act as their sources for analysis. Since worksheets are easy to correct, students may be able to recognize errors in the products and areas to correct such shortcomings. It's a smart idea to keep a record; as a parent, you will be able to go back through them and analyze their positive and weak areas. Holding watch, as scientific confirmation, you will be able to monitor the growth of your infant.

Online Free Worksheets for Math

The internet has countless possibilities to help the mathematical ability of your boy. There are several host worksheets on websites designed into games that will measure multiplication, fractions for them. Besides, they are arranged according to worksheet forms appropriate for your kids. Math can be daunting and exciting; it is an area where discipline and commitment must be in order. Regardless of how we stop algebra, it's there. Not all kids are born with gifted math skills, but there are always opportunities to help our kids understand, no matter how complicated math is. Good tools must be sought that will make teaching successful and faster.

Six ideas for fun and simple Child Math Activity

Math is a feature of daily life. We use arithmetic when shopping, measure the distance when driving, prepare a tasty meal, plant a garden, and play games. Children will learn math principles like estimating, word puzzles, time and distance, calculation, and simple addition and subtraction when playing games. Here are six different principles of child math operation that are basic and fun:

Counting activities involve throwing jelly beans in a big transparent container or candy corn. Have the children glance at the jar and guess the number of bits of candy they believe might be in the jar. Then count out the candy as a group to see who had the nearest estimate.

Play the game of guessing coins. Offer one of each form of the coin to each boy. Ask questions such as A nickel adds up to five of this coin. Ask tougher questions progressively until the child masters each question. By asking what coins make 35 cents, or how many pennies will he or she send you for a penny, exercise addition?

Point out speed limits and lengths to drive from one spot to another while traveling. Let them use a map to measure how long it would take for two towns to fly. When traveling at various speeds, let kids find out the time to drive a given distance.

Cooking is an excellent way to learn a lot of math skills. Let them help weigh our ingredients and speak to them about fractions. How many quarter cups in one cup are there? Create a pizza and chop it into 8 slices. How many slices does one half of the pie have? Chat with children about cooking hours and temperatures. Let them measure cold or hot food products using a thermometer.

Have them help with planting and determine how tall the crops are growing. To plant seeds a certain distance apart, they may use a measuring tape or ruler. Or make children draw their bedroom diagram and calculate how large the room is. Doorways, curtains, closets, etc. may be calculated.

Play tic-tac-toe, checkers, chess, board, and dice games, for instance. These games promote counting, pattern finding, and problem-solving. Drawing an amusing creature entails a friendly dice game. You need a pair of dices, plain paper, and markers to play the game. Kids will roll the dice and sum up the two numbers. Whatever the response is, on their paper, they will draw the corresponding creature element.

Rolling the number of 2 and drawing a nose

Roll and draw a mouth with the number of 3

Roll the number of 4 and attract ears

Roll 5 or 6 of the total and draw a leg

Rolling the total of 7 and drawing ahead

Rolling the number of 8 and drawing hair

Roll 9 in the total and draw a tail

Roll 10 or 11 of the total and draw an eye

Roll the 12th sum and draw an arm

To build a funny creature, each player should have at least six turns. Discuss their creatures afterward; how many eyes or legs do they have? When spinning the dice, they will also discuss the figures on whatever numbers have come up the most.

Lessons during a child's formative years are the most relevant during his entire stay in kindergarten. This provides the foundations of his social skills. This is why any teacher will do everything possible to make her topic as insightful and fascinating as possible. She would make use of materials and items that would engage the infant as best she could. In math, trends in a teacher's curriculum have been a staple.

Why patterns?

A pattern is characterized as any sequence which at least twice occurs in any given set of circumstances. The definition of patterns allows a child to understand. That is why the understanding of patterns was one of the underlying principles that had to be discussed during the infant's early education. In kindergarten or nursery, it's still present in the math subjects. Without someone instructing him to do so, an infant needs to recognize and establish trends. Via counting, the most fundamental way to instill this lesson to him is He or she would know that it begins at 0 and ends at 9, so it needs to go back to 0. He will understand a portion of the theory until he begins counting that goes beyond 10.

A kid would be able to grasp the other principles of math by pattern recognition quickly. It would be simpler to add, remove, and grasp. In evaluating and addressing word issues, he would obtain a profound understanding that is essential. If he does not remember patterns, even with the use of, let's say, the heuristic math system, solving a problem would prove to be a challenge. If he doesn't realize why this move can come before or after another step, he won't follow a protocol.

A sense of self-confidence in the infant can be instilled by pattern identification. Without the need to wait and continuously inquire for more guidance, he will learn what to do next. He's going to be able to forecast what happens next. This will allow him to pursue his learning with confidence and strive to solve new issues. He doesn't need to be so focused on his teacher, and this will inspire him, in the long term, to continue to improve and learn new things continually.

Activities for establishing recognition of a child's pattern

To enhance its pattern recognition, here are some activities that you can do with your boy.

1. The Beads

Bring beads in varying sizes and colors for you. After a pattern, you should ask your children to string the beads together. Start with the pattern of AB or ABC and go there from there.

2. Slice and paste

Bring assorted colored paperwork and scissors. Tell your children to cut from the rectangular paper forms. By asking them to do the forms in ascending order of height, you may do it further. Before they have to continue cutting the smallest rectangle again, it grows higher and taller. This will test their ability to distinguish sets of entity colors and heights.

## 3. Drawing Chalk

On the black side of the imageboard, they will sketch. Using colored chalks and teach them to draw circles using the rainbow color series. This will help them to recognize the color chain.

## 4. Toys

You carry different toys. Using actual things they are interested in, this will get them to understand the idea. Place them on the floor, arrange the toys-a doll, then a car, and then a book-in an ABC series. Line them up and ask the kid to place in the line the next object. The dolls don't need to be equal. They oughtn't to be. Only bring the assorted dolls in. It will help grow their appreciation further.

# CHAPTER 4: WHY SOME KIDS STRUGGLE WITH MATH WORD PROBLEMS

At a Glance

If kids have issues with math word problems, it does not mean they are bad at math.

Kids have to focus and read to solve a word problem in math.

Solving word problems is more than just doing calculations.

Word problems in mathematics can be tricky. To get the correct answer, children should be able to figure out what math operation to use, read the words, and then do the calculations. A breakdown in any of these skills can result to challenges.

If a kid seems to be good at mathematics but has challenges with word problems, below are possible reasons why—and ways to deal with it.

Trouble With Reading

Kids have to read properly to solve word problems. One reason kids struggle with maths is that they have trouble reading in general.

How do you know that this is a trouble point? Read a word problem to your child. If your child gets the right answer when you read it, but not when he reads it on their own, it could be a challenge with reading.

How you can help: Ask your kid's teacher to read word problems out loud for tests and classwork. This change can help your kid keep learning mathematics, even if reading is an issue. (You may decide to ask the school about technology that can read problems)

Also, there are also ways to help your kid improve reading skills at home.

Difficulty Understanding Math Concepts and Phrases

Even if children are solid readers, they may have trouble picking up on guide in word problems. These guides are phrases that help kids figure what they need to do to solve the problem. Kids must be able to translate these phrases into what teachers call "a number sentence."

Here is an instance of a word problem and its corresponding number sentence:

Word problem: "Susan has 2 pencils. She spends 1 hour at the store and buys 3 more pencils. How many pencils does Susan have in all?"

Number sentence: "3 + 2 = ____."

Some children can picture a number sentence like this in their heads. Others may need to write it down. Either way, there is a lot to think about before you get to the point where you figure the answer is 5.

To convert a word problem into a number sentence, kids need to understand the language and concepts of math. For instance, they need to know that the phrase "How many pencils in all?" means adding the two groups of pencils together.

Some kids have a lot of difficulties with this skill. That is why a child who can easily calculate 3 + 2 = 5 might struggle with a word problem using the exact calculation.

How you can help: Ask the school teacher to make index cards with phrases that are used in word problems. For instance, one index card might show "in all" next to the "+" sign. Another card may show "all together" next to the "+" sign.

When your kid works on math homework, encourage your kid to get into the habit of matching an index card to each phrase in a word problem.

Also, you can ask kids to close their eyes and picture what is happening in the problem: "Imagine the first set of pencils joining with the second group and forming one large group."

Some kids may have difficulty picturing this. You can make it more concrete by using toothpicks, coins, or other objects. Use them to form the 2 small groups, and then combine them into 1 group.

Trouble With Self-Control and Focus

Some kids can read a word problem and figure how it should be solved but still get the wrong answer. What's going on? One reason could be trouble with self control and focus.

Kids may get lost in their heads, or get distracted by the words. This can lead to confusion with math. Other kids struggle with self-control and just rush through the problem. They may skip vital parts or make simple calculation errors.

Extra details in word problems can trip kids up, too. Some details are not needed to solve the problem. For instance, kids do not need to know that Sue spent one hour in the store to know how many pencils she has. Kids should should learn to weed out this information.

How you can help: Ask your kid to read through the problem. Then, have him or her read it again, circling the important phrases and words. This is called active reading. It can help your kid stay focused and avoid rushing.

Here is another strategy. Use a piece of paper to cover all the problems except the one your child is doing. You can make a list of things for your kid to double-check. The teacher may also have more strategies, so don't be afraid to ask.

Once you have tried a few of these recommendations, you might have an idea why your kid is struggling with math word problems. Fix a meeting with the teacher about your concerns. Both of  can make a plan to help your kid get better at solving word problems.

**Key Takeaways**

Trouble reading can make it difficult to solve math word problems.

Using index cards can help children match phrases to different math operations.

Encourage your child to circle keywords and phrases in a problem to stay focused.

# CHAPTER 5: HOW TO HELP KIDS SOLVE MATH WORD PROBLEMS

I was working on multiplying and dividing by 2 with one of my kids recently. A constant refrain was, "What does multiply mean?" or "But remember, what does that division sign represent?"

As they started to grapple with these concepts and play with manipulatives and pictures and equations, I tried to make sure we always came back to the why. But why are you counting by 2's to get the answer? And why are we splitting our set into groups of 2? Or 2 equal groups?

Even after a high level of confidence in solving basic problems, when we began to work through math word problems, what do you think they did?

Pulled out all the numbers and added. Yes, added. Even for the division.

After spending so much time talking about multiplication and division and practicing with hands-on manipulatives and drawing pictures...the gut response to a word problem was to pull out the numbers without thinking and add them all together!

Is this ever true of your kids? Are they "number pluckers?" Or do they feel confident solving math word problems of every shape and form?

If you're looking for help teaching kids to solve word problems, here are some tips and ideas for you!

## THE GOAL OF MATH INSTRUCTION

I think this raises the question, "Why do we do this anyway???" Does it matter if children can solve word problems? Why can't we make the facts known? Well, I think our ultimate aim is not to generate fast and efficient machines (that's what calculators are for), but instead to create strong problem solvers.

To help grow critical thinkers and children who think outside the box and apply logical reasoning.

I love this quote from S.Y. Gillan from the book "Problems Without Figures:"

In arithmetic, any problem calls for two distinct and widely different kinds of work: first, the solution requires an understanding of the problem conditions and their relationship with each other; second, the process. First, we decide what to do; this requires logical reasoning. We do the work; this is simply a mechanical procedure; adding, multiplying, dividing, and subtracting does not train the ability to reason, but choosing which of these operations to use in a given set of conditions and why, is the arithmetic feature which requires reasoning.

Do you hear what he's saying? We are not just teaching children to do the work: the actual procedure of adding two numbers together. We are teaching children to reason and then apply their reasoning.

The Problem with Depending On Keywords in Math Word Problems

We have to help kids make sense of the situation while we spend deliberate time helping them make sense of word problems. That implies that we need to step away from relying on keywords. Why?

1. Depending on keywords can lead kids astray:

Even though teachers give children lists of keywords with the very best intentions, this is not helpful if they are used differently than kids are used to.

Here is an example. Say kids are given the following word problem:

William has nineteen toy cars. He has six less than his brother Bobby. How many toy cars does Bobby have?

Immediately, kids see two numbers: 19 and 6. They then see the keyword "less," and what operation we normally associate that keyword with? Subtraction.

Therefore, kids complete the problem by subtracting 6 from 19 for an answer of 13.

What is the problem here?

Well, in this case, to find the final solution, we need to add. Have you ever seen "less" listed on a keyword chart under addition? I haven't!

Not all math word problems include keywords: what about those problems that present a situation without an actual keyword? If kids are entirely dependent on keywords, they will just be lost!

Here's a great article that explains the problem with keywords and includes a helpful exercise to help kids think about the situation.

Although every word problem includes the term "total," they all require a different process and operation to solve it, forcing kids to think about the situation.

Real-life math doesn't include keywords:

Finally, looking for keywords isn't practical advice for real-world problem-solving. When our kids come against a situation in their life that requires mathematics, there will be no keywords.

Just messy, real life.

So what can we do?

Well, here are some questions you can ask and encourage your kids to ask as they seek to comprehend the situation rather than pluck out keywords or numbers:

- How would you describe the situation in your own words?

- How do you picture this problem in your mind?
- Can you draw a picture or model to represent this situation?

The goal is to really probe kids and force them to think about and picture the situation.

Yes, this takes more practice and work than plucking out numbers and keywords. But remember the end goal and press on!

Second, I have some math word problem-solving templates that you can use to help your kids think about the situation and then do the actual calculations.

There are a few different templates here, so I hope you find one that will meet your needs!

The goal of these templates is to help kids draw a picture of the situation and use that to come up with a logical plan to solve.

We don't want kids to throw logic and reasoning out the window. We want to encourage them to make reasonable strategies and decisions as they work out solutions.

Some include space to verify their answer as well.

# CHAPTER 6: MATH WORD PROBLEMS, CATEGORIZED BY SKILL

## ADDITION

1. Adding to 10: Maria was playing basketball. 2 of her shots went in the hoop. 1 of her shots didn't go in the hoop. How many shots were there in total?

2. Adding to 20: Lucy has 5 pieces of gum to share with her friends. There was not enough gum for all of them, so she went to the store to get 5 more pieces of gum. How many pieces of gum does Lucy have now?

3. Adding to 100: Lucy has 12 pieces of gum to share with her friends. There was not enough gum for all of them, so she went to the store and got 72 pieces of strawberry gum and 8 pieces of bubble gum. How many pieces of gum does Lucy have now?

4. Adding Slightly over 100: The restaurant has 165 normal chairs and 22 chairs for babies. In total, How many chairs does the restaurant have?

5. Adding to and over 10,000: Normally, the hobby store sells 11,576 trading cards per month. In June, the hobby store sold 14,498 more trading cards than normal. How many trading cards in total did the hobby store sell in June?

6. Adding to 1,000: How many biscuits did you sell if you sold 310 chocolate cookies and 280 vanilla cookies?

7. Adding 3 Numbers: Liza had 2 books at home. She went to the library to take out 1 more book. Then, he bought 2 books. How many books does Bobby have now?

8. Adding 3 Numbers to and over 100: Cara purchased a big bag of candy. The bag had 104 red

candies, 101 green candies, and 74 blue candies. How many candies were there in total?

9. In a school there are 524 boys and 432 girls. What is the number of students in this school. Answer = _____

10. Olivia played a car game and scored 330 points in first round and 451 points in second round. The game was over after the second round. How many points did she have at the end of the game?
Answer = _____

11. James got $225 from her father and $480 from her mother. How much money does she have now?
Answer = _____

12. There are 150 lions and 131 leopard in a forest. These are the only wild animals in the forest. What is the total number of wild animals in the forest.
Answer = _____

13. A movie rental shop has 6216 old DVDs and 5433 new DVDs. Find the total number of DVDs in the shop? Answer = _____

14. In a public telephone booth, 443 calls are made before noon and 289 calls are made after noon. What is the number of calls made in a day. Answer = _____

15. In a grand musical show, 1301 men and 1289 women participated. What is the total number of participants? Answer = _____

16. James jogs 1200 m and runs 1500 m. Find the total distance covered. Answer = _____

17. A famous dictionary contains 2012 pages. A new version includes 2003 more pages. Find the total number of pages in a new version? Answer = _____

18. There are 4289 birds in a bird sanctuary. 2438 more birds join during summer. Find the number of birds in summer. Answer = _____

19. Mr. Bryson wrote a book on Fairy Tales and released 60, 535 copies. Because the book was popular, the publishers decided to publish a second edition with 40, 399 copies. Find the total number of copies published. Answer =

_____

20. A company manufactures 423,500 bolts on Monday and 224,800 bolts on Tuesday. What is the total number of bolts manufactured on those two days. Answer = _____

21. The population of a New York City was 7,363,710 in 2008. It was expected to increase by 2,201,977 by the end of 2010. What was the expected population of New York City at the end of 2010? Answer = _____

22. In the society library, there are 498,456 old books. The management decided to add 65,875 new books. How many books will be there in library? Answer = _____

## SUBTRACTION

23. An animal care society tested 456 pet animals. 227 were infected by diseases. What is the number of healthy pet animals that participated in the medical tests. Answer = _____

24. A shopkeeper bought 340 eggs and sold 248 eggs. How many eggs were left unsold? Answer = _____

25. In an annual celebration, 573 students participated. Of them, 293 were boys. Find the number of girls who participated. Answer = _____

26. Director Mike directed a film which ran for 228 minutes. During the editing process, 119 minutes were removed. What is the final running time of the film? Answer = _____

27. Bob has a book which contains 549 pages. He has already read 395 pages. How many pages are unread? Answer = _____

28. There are 6718 DVDs in Mr. Miller's shop. 1199 are audio DVDs and the rest of them are video DVDs. What is the number of video DVDs in Mr. Biden's shop. Answer = _____

29. Dora withdrew $ 5789 from her account. The initial amount in her account was $ 9790. How much is left after the withdrawal. Answer =

_____

30. Jane needs at least 2000 points to go to level 3 in a video game. She has only 2254 points in level 2.

How many more points does she need to qualify for level 3? Answer = _____

31. A free medical camp was conducted in Mexico. 2278 males participated in the camp. The entry book shows 5012 people participated in the camp. Find the number of females who participated. Answer = _____

32. What is the difference between the smallest six-digit whole number and the greatest 4-digit whole number? Answer = _____

33. The average distance from earth to the sun is 92, 589, 230 miles. The distance from earth to the moon is 92,350,373 miles less than the distance from earth to the sun. What is the distance from earth to the moon. Answer = _____

34. Laura bought a brand new car for $30,086. The estimated value of the car after 6 years is $14,990. If she sells the car after 6 years, by how much less money would she have? Answer = _____

35. Mr. Mason donates $2,599 by check for Haiti relief fund. The amount in his account is $208,456. How much will be left in the account once the check is released? Answer = _____

36. Subtracting to 10: There were 4 pizzas in total at the pizza shop. A customer purchased 2 pizza. How many pizzas are left?

37. Subtracting to 20: Your friend said he had 12 stickers. When you helped him clean his desk, he only had a total of 8 stickers. How many stickers are missing?

38. Subtracting to 100: Leonard has 90 pieces of gum to share with his friends. When she went to the park, he shared 12 pieces of strawberry gum. When he left the park, Leonard shared another 12 pieces of bubble gum. How many pieces of gum does Leonard have now?

39. Subtracting Slightly over 100: Your school team scored a total of 112 points. 72 points were scored

in the second half. How many were scored in the first half?

40. Subtracting to 1,000: Cara has a big ant farm. She decided to sell some of her ants. She started with 975 ants. She sold 220. How many ants does she have now?

41. Subtracting to and over 10,000: An hobby store normally sells 11,576 trading cards monthly. The hobby store sold a total of 19,777 trading cards in July. How many more trading cards did the hobby store sell in July compared with a normal month?

42. Subtracting 3 Numbers to and over 100: Michael bought a big bag of candy to share with his friends. In total, there were 286 candies. He gave 102 candies to Marissa. He also gave 77 candies to Leo. How many candies were left?

43. Subtracting 3 Numbers: John had a pack of 45 crayons. He gave 8 to his friend Bob. She gave 4 to

his friend Mandy. How many crayons does Charlene have left?

## MULTIPLICATION

Directions | Read each question carefully, identify the key information, show all of your work, and circle your final answer!

44. Multiplying 1-Digit Integers:  Anderson needs to cut a pan of brownies into pieces. He cuts 8 even columns, and 4 even rows into the pan. How many brownies does he have?

45. Multiplying 2-Digit Integers: A movie theatre has 30 rows of seats with 10 seats in each row. How many seats are there in total?

46. Multiplying 3 Integers: A bricklayer stacks bricks in 4 rows, with 15 bricks in each row. On top of each row, there is a stack of 5 bricks. How many bricks are there in total?

47. Multiplying Integers Ending with 0: A clothing organization has 5 different kinds of sweatshirts. The organization makes 50,000 of each kind of sweatshirt yearly. How many sweatshirts does the organization make each year?

48. Multiplying 4 Integers: Bob earns $5 an hour by delivering newspapers. He delivers newspapers 3 days weekly, for 4 hours at a time. After delivering newspapers for 8 weeks, how much money will Bob earn?

49. Caroline baked 7 batches of cupcakes on Saturday. Then, on Sunday, she baked 3 times as many batches of cupcakes as she did on Saturday. How many batches of cupcakes did she bake on Sunday?

50. There are three school buses taking students on a field trip to the zoo. If each bus holds 12 students, how many total students are going on the field trip?

51. Fernando is buying several boxes of cookies for a birthday party. There are 9 cookies in each box. If Fernando brings 7 boxes to the party, how many cookies is he bringing?

52. Luigi's Pizzeria sells combo meals for $4 each. How much would it cost to order ten combo meals?

53. Calvin is organizing his baseball cards into stacks of ten cards each. How many baseball cards does he have if he can make 12 stacks?

54. A movie theatre has 9 rows of seats. In each row, there are 11 seats. How many total seats are in the movie theatre?

## DIVISION

Directions | Carefully read each question, identify the key information, show all of your work, and circle your final answer!

55. Dividing 1-Digit Integers: If you have 6 pieces of candy split evenly into 3 bags, how many pieces of candy are in each bag?

56. Dividing Numbers Ending with 0: The school has $30,000 to buy new computer equipment. If each piece of equipment costs $100, how many pieces can the school buy in total?

57. Dividing 2-Digit Integers: If you have 100 tickets for the fair and each ride costs 10 tickets, how many rides can you go on?

58. Dividing 3 Integers: Mary buys 3 packs of tennis balls for $15 in total. Altogether, there are 6 tennis balls. How much does 1 tennis ball cost? How much does 1 pack of tennis balls cost?

59. Caroline baked a sheet of 20 chocolate chip cookies to share with her 4 friends. If she gave an

equal amount of cookies to each friend, how many cookies did each person get?

60. Kelsi plays video games for the same amount of time every day. Over the last 7 days, she played a total of 21 hours of video games. How many hours of video games did she play each day?

61. Cristiano is throwing a pizza party for his friends. He orders a total of 36 slices of pizza for the nine people who will be at the party. If everyone is given the same number of slices, how many slices of pizza can each person have?

62. Augustine is selling his baseball cards at a yard sale. He is selling his cards for $3 each. At the end of the yard sale, he made $60. How many baseball cards did he sell?

63. Jean has a truckload of watermelons to deliver. He has a total of 100 watermelons in his truck and has to deliver the same amount of watermelons to

4 different grocery stores, how many watermelons will each store receive?

64. Debbie waters her houseplants several times throughout the day. Over the past 50 days, she watered her plants a total of 200 times. How many times does she water her houseplants each day?

MEASUREMENT

Directions | Carefully read each question, identify the key information, show all of your work, and circle your final answer!

66. A rope is 36 inches long. If the rope was cut into 4 equal pieces, how long would each piece be?

67. Kelsi's houseplant grew 10cm since last month. If her houseplant was 26cm tall last month, how tall is it now?

68. When John was five years old, he was 3 feet tall. When John turned 15, he was two times as tall as he was when he was five. How tall was John at age 15?

69. Lisa's pet snake, Slippy, is 24 inches long. How many feet long is Slippy?

70. The tallest slide at the park is ten feet tall. How many inches tall is the slide?

71. There are three kinds of vines growing in Georgia's back yard. The first vine is 50cm long. The second vine is 8cm longer than the first vine. And the third vine is 12 cm longer than the second vine. How long is the third vine?

# CHAPTER 7: MATH WORD PROBLEMS FOR THIRD GRADERS.

Here is a selection of some of the tallest trees in the world today.

| Tree | Height (m) |
|---|---|
| Australian Mountain Ash | |
| Coast Douglas Fir | 99 |
| Coast Redwood | 116 |
| Giant Sequoia | |
| Manna Gum | 89 |
| Sitka Spruce | |
| Tasmanian Blue Gum | 91 |

1. Use the data below to complete the missing information in the table.

- The Sitka Spruce is 8m taller than the Manna Gum tree.

- The Giant Sequoia is 21m shorter than the Coast Redwood.

- The Australian Mountain Ash is 11m taller than the Manna Gum.

2. Put the trees in order of height, from 1 to 7, with 1 being the shortest and 7 being the tallest.
3. How much taller is the Coast Redwood than the Sitka Spruce? ___ m
4. How much shorter is the Manna Gum than the Coast Redwood? ___ m
5. Tyger climbs halfway up a tree. He is 45½m off the ground. Which tree has he climbed? _____
6. The height of a mature oak tree is about 21m. Tyger says "The Coast

Redwood is taller than 5 mature oak trees._" Is he correct? _____

Here is a selection of some of the tallest lighthouses in the world today.

| Lighthouse | Height (ft |
|---|---|
| Ile Vierge | 271 |
| Jeddah Light | |
| Lighthouse of Genoa | |
| Perry Memorial Monument | 352 |
| Phare de Gatteville | 247 |
| Yokohama Marine Tower | |

1) Use these facts to complete the table above:

- The Lighthouse of Genoa is 18ft lower than the Ile Vierge.

- The Jeddah Light is 84ft higher than the Perry Memorial Monument.

- The Yokohama Marine Tower is 61ft higher than the Ile Vierge.

2) Fill in the order of height from 1 to 6, with 1 being the tallest.

3) How much taller is the Perry Memorial Monument than the Phare de Gatteville? _____ ft

4) How much shorter is the Ile Vierge than the Jeddah Light? _____ ft

5) Tyger says "The Jeddah Light is more than double the height of the shortest tower." Is he correct? _____

6) Which tower is closest to 300ft in height?

   _____

7) Tyger says "If you put three Yokohama towers on top of each other, it would make about 1000ft." Is he correct? _____

Captain Salamander goes on a long journey around the world. He travels ¼ of the journey by plane, and the rest by boat. What fraction of the journey does he travel by boat?

1)     Whilst on the boat, Captain Salamander spends his free time watching TV and swimming.

He spends $\frac{3}{8}$ of his free time watching TV. What fraction of his free time does he spend swimming?

2)     When swimming, Captain Salamander likes to spend most of his time underwater. He only spends $\frac{1}{10}$ of his time above water. What fraction of his time swimming is spent underwater?

3)     His favourite drink is a mixture of cranberry juice and water. He drink is $\frac{2}{5}$ cranberry juice. What fraction of the drink is water?

4)     Captain Salamander shares a box of chocolates with some friends he has met up with. He gives his friends $\frac{4}{9}$ of the chocolates. What fraction does he have left?

5)     On the boat, he eats a diet of crayfish and fish eggs. About $\frac{2}{7}$ of his diet is fish eggs. What fraction of his diet is crayfish?

6)     Captain Salamander has a lazy time on the trip and spends about 15 hours a day sleeping. What fraction of the day does he spend awake?

7)     If $\frac{7}{10}$ of the passengers on the boat are male, what fraction are female?

Here are facts about some of the members of the cat family.

| Name | Average Weight (kg) |
|---|---|
| Cheetah | |
| Lynx | 26 |
| Lion | 190 |
| Cougar | 73 |
| Leopard | 67 |
| Tiger | |

1) Use the information below to complete the information in the table:

- The cheetah is 7kg lighter than a leopard.

- The tiger can run 13kph faster than a lynx.

- The tiger is 37kg heavier than a lion.

2) Put the animals in order of weight, from lightest to heaviest.

_____  _____  _____  _____  _____

_____

3) How much heavier is a cougar than a lynx?
\_\_\_\_ kg

4) How much faster is a cheetah than a leopard?
\_\_\_\_ kph

5) Tyger says "The cheetah is more than twice as fast as a leopard." Is he right? \_\_\_\_

6) Tyger says "A lion is a faster and heavier animal than a tiger." Is he right? \_\_\_\_

7) Tyger says "A cougar would be heavier than 3 lynxes." Is he right? \_\_\_\_

Here are some of the tallest buildings throughout history.

| Name of building | Year | W |
|---|---|---|
| Great Pyramid of Giza | 2570 BC | Egy |
| Lincoln Cathedral | 1311 | En |
| Washington Monument | 1884 | US |
| Eiffel Tower | | Frar |
| Chrysler Building | 1930 | US |
| Empire State Building | 1931 | US |
| Ostankino Tower | | Rus |
| CN Tower | | Ca |
| Burj Khalifa | 2007 | Dut |

1) Use the information below to complete the missing data in the table.

- The Eiffel Tower was built 5 years after the Washington Monument.

- Washington Monument is 9m taller than Lincoln Cathedral.

- The Great Pyramid was 14m lower than Lincoln Cathedral.

- Ostankino Tower was built 36 years after the Empire State Building.

- The CN Tower is 16m taller than the Ostankino Tower and was built 45 years after the Chrysler Building.

2) Round all the heights to the nearest 10m and fill in the column.

3) How much taller is the Eiffel Tower than the Washington Monument?

_____ m

4) Tyger says "The Burj Khalifa is taller than the Chrysler Building and the Empire State Building put together." Is he correct? Why?

# TALLEST HISTORICAL BUILDINGS (METRIC) ANSWERS

| Name of building | Year | W |
|---|---|---|
| Great Pyramid of Giza | 2570 BC | Egy |
| Lincoln Cathedral | 1311 | En |
| Washington Monument | 1884 | US |
| Eiffel Tower | 1889 | Fran |
| Chrysler Building | 1930 | US |
| Empire State Building | 1931 | US |
| Ostankino Tower | 1967 | Rus |
| CN Tower | 1975 | Ca |
| Burj Khalifa | 2007 | Dub |

1) Use the information below to complete the missing data in the table.

- The Eiffel Tower was built 5 years after the Washington Monument.

- Washington Monument is 9m taller than Lincoln Cathedral.

- The Great Pyramid was 14m lower than Lincoln Cathedral.

- Ostankino Tower was built 36 years after the Empire State Building.

- The CN Tower is 16m taller than the Ostankino Tower and was built 45 years after the Chrysler Building.

2) Round all the heights to the nearest 10m and fill in the column.

3) How much taller is the Eiffel Tower than the Washington Monument?

131 m

4) Tyger says "The Burj Khalifa is taller than the Chrysler Building and the Empire State Building put together." Is he correct? Burj Khalifa = 830m Chrysler + Empire = 319 + 381 = 700m. He is correct.

Here are some of the tallest buildings throughout history.

| Name of building | Year | Wh |
|---|---|---|
| Great Pyramid of Giza | 2570 BC | Egyp |
| Lincoln Cathedral | 1311 | Eng |
| Washington Monument | 1884 | US |
| Eiffel Tower | | Fran( |
| Chrysler Building | 1930 | US |
| Empire State Building | 1931 | US |
| Ostankino Tower | | Russi |
| CN Tower | | Ca |
| Burj Khalifa | 2007 | Dub; |

1) Use the information below to complete the missing data in the table.

- The Eiffel Tower was built 5 years after the Washington Monument.

- Washington Monument is 29ft taller than Lincoln Cathedral.

- The Great Pyramid was 46ft lower than Lincoln Cathedral.

- Ostankino Tower was built 36 years after the Empire State Building.

- The CN Tower is 52ft taller than the Ostankino Tower and was built 45 years after the Chrysler Building.

2) Round all the heights to the nearest 10ft and fill in the column.

3) How much taller is the Eiffel Tower than the Washington Monument?
_____ ft

4) Tyger says "The Burj Khalifa is taller than the Chrysler Building and the Empire State Building put together." Is he correct?

# CHAPTER 8: WORD PROBLEMS EXPLAINED FOR PRIMARY SCHOOL PARENTS AND

# TEACHERS

What is a word problem?

A word problem in mathematics is a math question written as one sentence or

more that requires kids to apply their knowledge of mathematics to a 'real-life' scenario.

This implies that, in order to make sense of the word dilemma, kids must be familiar with the vocabulary associated with the mathematical symbols they are used to.

For instance:

# Vocabulary Used In Wor

| If you see this word/phrase... | .. |
|---|---|
| Add a surplus, more, total, and, together, sum, increase by... | |
| difference between, reduce, fewer, minus, decrease... | |
| share, equal groups, split... | |
| product, groups of, lots of... | |

Isn't brilliant arithmetic enough?

In short, no.

The National Curriculum specifies that its mathematics curriculum "aims to ensure that pupils:

Become proficient in fundamentals of mathematics, including through varied and regular practice with increasingly complex issues over time, so that pupils develop conceptual understanding and the ability to efficiently and precisely recall and apply knowledge;

Reason mathematically by following a line of inquiry, conjecturing relationships and generalizations and using mathematical language to establish an argument, justification or proof;

By applying their mathematics to a number of routine and non-routine issues with increasing complexity, they can solve problems, including breaking down problems into a series of easier steps and persevering in finding solutions.

A 'mastery' approach to mathematics is being introduced to benefit these schools.

The National Centre for Excellence in the Teaching of Mathematics have defined "teaching for mastery", with some aspects of this definition being:

Maths teaching for mastery rejects the notion that a significant number of individuals can't just do maths.'

All pupils are inspired by the idea that by working hard at maths they will excel.

Procedural fluency and conceptual understanding are established since each promotes the growth of the other.

Significant time is spent gaining a comprehensive understanding of the main ideas needed to underpin future learning. Within mathematics, the structure and ties are illustrated, so that pupils develop deep learning that can be maintained.

(The Essence of Maths Teaching for Mastery, 2016)

Mastery encourages children to learn math in full depth.

"Mathematical Thinking is one of NCETM 's Five Major Ideas in Teaching for Mastery (2017):" If taught ideas are to be understood profoundly, they must not only be received passively, but the pupil must work on them: thought about, reason with, and debate with others.

In other words, indeed, arithmetic fluency is essential; but with this, the common belief also lies that once a child has mastered the number skills appropriate to their level / age, they should be advanced to the next level / age of number skills.

Via reasoning and problem solving, the mastery strategy promotes exploring the scope and depth of these concepts (once fluency is secure).

See the example below:

| Year 6 objective | Fluency | Reasoning | Problem solving |
|---|---|---|---|
| Solve addition and subtraction multi-step problems in contexts, deciding which operations and methods to use and why. | 7,208 females attended a concert as well as 8,963 males. There were originally 20,000 seats on sale. How | Abdul says, "If I add any two 4-digit numbers together, it will make a 5-digit number." Do you agree? Explain | Three pandas are eating bamboo sticks. There are 51 altogether. They all eat an odd number of sticks. How |

| Year 6 objective | Fluency | Reasoning | Problem solving |
|---|---|---|---|
| | many empty seats were there at the concert? | why. | many bamboo sticks did they each eat? How many different ways can you do it? |

What kind of word problems would my kid encounter in school?

There are nine 'strands' of math in Key Stage 2, which are then further divided into 'sub-strands'. "For example, the first strand is 'number and place value': a Year 3 sub-strand of this is to "find 10 or 100 more or less than a given number"; a Year 6 sub-strand of this is to "determine in numbers up to 10 million the value of each digit. The following table illustrates how the 'sub-strands' are distributed in KS2 across each strand and year group.

| Strand | Year 3 | Year 4 | Year 5 | Year 6 | Total |
|---|---|---|---|---|---|
| Number and place value | 6 | 9 | 7 | 5 | 27 |
| Calculations | 7 | 8 | 15 | 9 | 39 |
| Fractions, decimals and percentages | 7 | 10 | 12 | 11 | 40 |
| Ratio and proportion | 0 | 0 | 0 | 4 | 4 |

| Strand | Year 3 | Year 4 | Year 5 | Year 6 | Total |
|---|---|---|---|---|---|
| Algebra | 0 | 0 | 0 | 5 | 5 |
| Measurement | 17 | 9 | 10 | 8 | 44 |
| Geometry: properties of shape | 5 | 4 | 6 | 7 | 22 |
| Geometry: position and direction | 0 | 3 | 1 | 2 | 6 |
| Statistics | 2 | 2 | 2 | 2 | 8 |

How to teach kids to solve word problems?

Here are two basic methods that can be applied to several word problems before solving them.

• What do you know already?

How can this problem be pictorially drawn / represented?

Let's see how to apply this to word problems to help achieve the answer.


Solving a basic word problem.

- The teacher has 8 litres of orange juice.
- She pours 225 millilitres of orange juice for every pupil.
- How much orange juice is left over?


1. What do you know?

- There are 1,000ml in one litre
- Pours = liquid leaving the bottle = subtraction
- Left over = requires subtraction at some point
- For every = multiply


2. How can this problem be pictorially drawn / represented?

The bar model is always a brilliant way of describing problems, but there are

always other ways to draw it out if you are not familiar with this.

For instance, for this question, you might draw 28 pupils (or stick man x 28) with '225 ml' above each one and then a half-empty bottle with '8 liters' marked at the top.

To put maths to work now.

This is a multi-step problem of Year 6, so we need to use

what we already know and what we have learnt to break down the steps.

There are 28 pupils in a class.

The teacher has 8 litres of orange juice.
☐ 1) 8 litres = 8,000ml

She pours 225 millilitres of orange juice every pupil.
☐ 2) 225ml x 28 = 6,300ml

How much orange juice is left over?
☐ 3) 8,000ml – 6,300ml = **1,700ml**

Solving a more complex word problem

Joe is in a bookshop.

He buys one book for £6.99 and another that costs £3.40 more than the first book.

He pays using a £20 notes.

What change does Joe get?

1. What do you already know?

- Using decimals means I'll have to line up the decimal points correctly in calculations
- More than = add
- Change from money = subtract

2. How can this problem be represented pictorially/drawn?

See this example of bar modelling for this question:

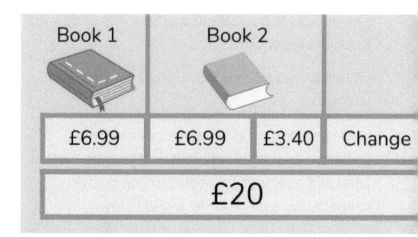

Now to put the maths to work using what we already know and what we have drawn to break down the steps.

Joe is in a bookshop.

He buys one book for £6.99 and another that costs £3.40 more than the first book. 1) £6.99 + (£6.99 + £3.40) = £17.38

He pays using a £20 note.

What change does Joe get? 2) £20 – £17.38 = £2.62

## Maths Word Problems For Years 1 to Year 6

The more kids learn about mathematics as they go through elementary

school, the trickier the word problems they face will get.

Some information about the types of word problems your child will face on a year-by-year basis and how word problems relate to each primary year group can be found below.

Word problems in Year 1

A child is likely to be exposed to word problems in Year 1 with the assistance of

concrete resources (pieces of physical apparatus such as counters, coins, cards, or number lines) to help them better understand the problem.

For Year 1, an example of a word problem would be:

Bob is going to buy his mum a cake that costs 80p. How many 20p coins would be needed to do this?

Word problems in Year Two

Year 2 is a continuation of Year 1 In terms of word problems, with kids also

using basic tools to help them understand and interpret the problems they are working on.

For Year 2, an example of a word problem would be:

A class of 15 children each have 3 pencils in their pencil cases. How many pencils are there in total?

Word problems in Year 3

In Year 3, kids can move away from using specific tools and move towards using written methods when addressing word problems.

Teachers would illustrate the four operations (addition, subtraction , multiplication and division problems).

This is also the year in which two-step problems will be introduced. This is a problem which requires 2 individual calculations to be completed.

WORD PROBLEMS WORKSHEET YEAR 3

Year Three word problem: Geometry properties of shape

Caroline is making 3-D shapes out of plastic straws.

At the vertices where the straws meet, she uses blobs of modelling clay to fix them together

Here are some of the shapes she makes:

| Shape | Number of straws | Number of blobs of modelling clay |
|-------|------------------|-----------------------------------|
| A | 8 | 5 |
| B | 12 | 8 |
| C | 6 | 4 |

One of Caroline's shapes is a cuboid. Which is it? Explain your answer.

Answer: shape B as a cuboid has twelve edges (straws) and eight vertices (clay)

Year Three word problem: Statistics

Year three are collecting pebbles. This pictogram below shows the different numbers of pebbles each group finds.

Year 3 children are collecting pebble
pictogram shows the different numb
pebbles each group finds.

| Group | Number of pebbles |
|-------|-------------------|
| A | ⬤⬤⬤⬤⬤⬤⬤ |
| B | ⬤⬤⬤⬤⬤ |
| C | ⬤⬤⬤⬤⬤⬤⬤⬤⬤ |
| D | |

⬤ = 2 pepples

**a** How many pebbles were collected b
Group B?

p

**b** Group D collected $\frac{1}{3}$ of the number
of pebbles that Group C collected.

Complete the pictogram to show thi

Answer: a) 9   b) 3 pebbles drawn

By the time kids are in Year 3, many of the word problems appear to be a variation on a multiplication problem, including one-step story problems. For this reason, learning tables becomes increasingly relevant at this point. To help with Year 3 maths at home, one of the best things you can do is help your child to do this.

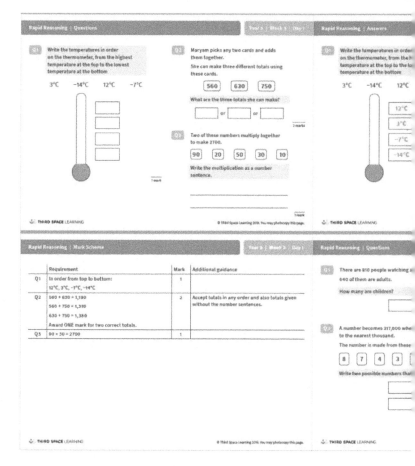

## Word problems worksheet Year 5

Year 5 word problem: Decimals, percentages, and fractions.

Emma, Olivia, and Ava are washing their cars outside their houses.

Ava has washed 5% of her car.

Olivia has washed 1/5 of her car.

Emma has washed 0.5 of her car.

Who has washed the most?

Explain your answer.

Answer: Emma (he has washed 0.5 whereas Olivia has only washed 0.2 and Ava 0.05)

Word problems in Year Six

In Year Six children move on from Two-step word problems to multi-step word problems. These will include decimals, percentages, and fractions.

Here are few examples of the types of maths word problems Year six will have to solve.

**Year Six word problem – Ratio and proportion**

This question is from the 2019 KS2 SATs paper. It is worth 1 mark.

The Angel of the North is a large statue in England. It is 54 metres wide and 20 metres tall.

Bobby makes a scale model of the Angel of the North. His model is 40 centimetres tall. How wide is his model?

Answer: 108cm

Year Six word problem – Algebra

This question is from the 2019 KS2 SATs paper. It is worth 2 marks as there are two parts to the answer.

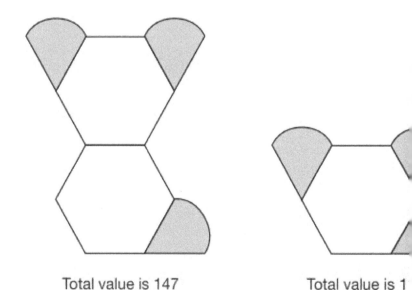

Total value is 147

Total value is 1

Laura is making designs with 2 different shapes.

She gives each shape a value.

Calculate the value of each shape.

Answer: 36 (hexagon) and 25.

Year Six word problem: Measurement

This question is from the 2019 KS2 SATs paper. It is worth 4 marks as it is a multi-step problem.

There are 28 students in a class.

The teacher has 8 litres of orange juice.

The teacher pours 225 millilitres of orange juice for every pupil.

How much orange juice is left over?

Answer: 1.7 litres or 1,700ml

# CHAPTER 9: TOPIC BASED WORD PROBLEMS

The following examples will give you an insight into the kinds of maths word problems kids will encounter for each of the nine strands of maths in KS2.

Place value word problem Year Five

This machine subtracts one hundredth every time the button is pressed. The starting number is 9.43. What number will the machine display if the button is pressed eight times? Answer: 9.35

## WORD PROBLEM YEAR THREE

1. Sam has 364 sweets. He gets given 142 more. He then gives 277 away. How many sweets is he left with?
2. Lara thinks of a number. She subtracts 70. Her new number is 12. What was the number Lara thought of?
3. A baker is baking chocolate cupcakes. She melts 16 chocolate buttons to make the icing for 9 cakes. How many chocolate buttons will she need to melt to make the icing for 18 cakes?
4. Leo and Bill both have bottles of strawberry smoothie. Each bottle contains 1 liter. Lucy drinks ½ of his bottle.

Bill drinks 300ml of his bottle. How much does each person have left in both bottles?

5. Lauren and James have different amounts of money. Lauren has twelve 2p coins. James has seven 5p coins. Who has the most money and by how much?

## WORD PROBLEM YEAR FOUR

1. Eggs are sold in boxes of 15. The egg boxes are taken to stores in crates. Each crate holds 10 boxes. How many eggs are in a crate?

2. The swimming pool at the Sunshine Inn hotel is 20m long and 7m wide. Mary swims around the edge of the pool twice. How many meters has she swum?

3. A rectangle measures 6cm by 5cm.

5cm

6cm

What is its area?

## WORD PROBLEM YEAR FIVE

1. A chocolate factory has 1 and 2/6 boxes of chocolate leftover at the end of every day. How many boxes of chocolates are leftover by the end of a week?
2. There are 400 children in a school. 50% are girls. How many girls are there?

## WORD PROBLEM YEAR 6

1. The temperature at 7 pm was 4oC. By midnight, it had dropped by 9 degrees. What was the temperature at midnight?

2. A factory produces 1,555 paintbrushes every day. They are packaged into boxes of 5. How many boxes does the factory produce daily?

3. Which two decimals that have a difference of 0.5? 0.2, 0.25, 0.4, 0.45, 0.6, 0.75.

4. A local council has spent the day painting double yellow lines. They use 1 pot of yellow paint for every 100m of the road they paint. How many pots of paint will they need to paint a 2km stretch of road?

5. This large cuboid has been made by stacking shipping containers on a boat. Each shipping container has a length of 6m, a width of 4m, and a height of 3m. What is the volume of the large cuboid?

How vital are word problems when it comes to the SATs?

In the KS1 SATs, 58 percent (35/60 marks) of the test comprises maths' reasoning' (word problems).

In KS2, this increases to 64 percent (70/110 marks) spread over two reasoning papers, each worth 35 marks. Considering kids have, in the past, needed approximately 55-60 percent to reach the 'expected standard,' it is clear that children need regular exposure to and a solid comprehension of how to solve a variety of word problems.

Remember: The word problems can change, but the maths won't

When children first come across word problems in KS2, they can be easily confused, but you must inform them that while the meaning of the problem can be interpreted differently, the math behind it remains the same.

Word issues are a great way to put mathematics into the real world and make your child's maths more important, so help them practice, or even ask them to turn the tables and come up with some word problems for you to solve.

# CHAPTER 10: ADDITION ACTIVITIES FOR KIDS MATH

1. James loves collecting small stuffed animals. She has 5 pigs and 8 hens. How many animals does he have in her collection?

2. A fish tank contains 5 large fish and 44 small fish. How many fish are there in the tank?

3. There are 16 sparrows and 41 eagles in Woods. How many birds are there in the Woods?

4. There are 6 cats and 4 sheep on a farm. How many animals are on the farm?

5. A zoo has 5 African elephants and 3 Indian elephants. How many elephants are in the zoo?

6. Mr. Nath drove 12 miles in his new car on Tuesday and 27 miles on Thursday. How many miles did he drive in these two days?

7. There are 8 trucks and 70 cabs in a parking lot. How many vehicles are in the parking lot?

8. There are 49 men and 45 women in an bus. How many passengers are there altogether?

9. Mike is a mechanic. He repaired 33 vans and 45 buses last month. How many vehicles did he repair altogether?

10. Mr. Smith used 5 gallons of fuel last week. She used 6 gallons this week. How many gallons of fuel were consumed in the two weeks?

11. A board game contains 15 green coins, 17 red coins, and 20 blue coins. How many coins are there in all?

**12.** Lola borrowed from the library 28 books on Thursday, 10 books on Friday, and 7 books on Saturday. How many books did she borrow altogether?

**13.** Mr. Bryan delivered 23 letters in May, 23 letters in June, and 23 letters in August. How many letters did she deliver in the three months?

**14.** For her new kitchen, Mrs. Ruth bought a cutlery set, a crockery set, and a pressure cooker. Each item cost $40 . How many dollars did she spend?

**15.** Greg played for 8 hours, Jack played for 8 hours, and Edward played 7 hours more than Greg. How many hours did they play altogether?

Herbert was involved in 54 thefts last year and 6 thefts this year. His parrot helped him steal 18 diamonds last year and 43 diamonds this year. He rewarded the parrot with an elastic band and some nuts. The parrot stretched the elastic band which was 11 inches long by another 8 inches. The parrot then ate 12 nuts. There are still 29 nuts left in the cage. It cost $ 2 to feed the parrot last week. This week it cost $ 10 more.

**16.** In two years, how many diamonds did the parrot steal?

**17.** In two years, how many thefts was the thief involved in?

**18.** How many dollars did it cost to feed the parrot for two weeks?

**19.** With how many nuts did the thief reward the parrot?

**20.** How many inches did the parrot stretch the elastic band to?

The table shows quiz marks out of 25 in each subject.

| | English Language | English Literature | Mathematics | Science |
|---|---|---|---|---|
| John | 22 | 21 | 9 | 7 |

| Andy | 23 | 7 | 24 | 16 |
| Jimmy | 14 | 21 | 25 | 22 |

**21.** What are the lowest total marks in English?

**22.** What are the highest total marks in English?

**23.** What are the lowest total marks in Mathematics and Science?

**24.** What are the lowest total marks in all four subjects?

**25.** What are the highest total marks in all four subjects?

26. There are 22 bananas and 40 mangoes in a fruit basket. How many total fruits are there in the basket?

27. Mr Joe used 70 pineapples and 2 apples to make fruit juice. How many fruits did she use to make juice?

28. Mrs. Kate has 14 apples and 43 oranges for sale in his fruit shop. How many fruits is that altogether?

29. A farmer has 34 apple trees and 6 plum trees in his orchard. How many trees is that altogether?

**30.** William ate 5 peaches and 7 apples over the weekend. How many fruits did he eat over the weekend?

**31.** Laura made a necklace for her doll using 34 green beads and 41 yellow beads. How many beads does the necklace have?

**32.** Evelyn has two dolls. The first doll costs $4 and the second costs $7. How many dollars do the two dolls cost?

**33.** Bob empties 15 marbles from a small box into a big box that already contains 46 marbles. How many marbles are now there in the big box?

**34.** Liham arranges 32 blocks in four stacks. He then arranges 14 blocks in six stacks. How many blocks did he arrange in the ten stacks?

**35.** Jack likes toy vehicles. He has 64 buses and 2 vans. How many toy vehicles does he have?

**36.** Mr. Bob drove 39 miles in his new car on Thursday and 32 miles on Monday. How many miles did he drive in these two days?

**37.** There are 8 vans and 42 buses in a parking lot. How many vehicles are there in the parking lot?

**38.** There are 5 men and 42 women in an aeroplane. How many passengers are there altogether?

**39.** Leonard is a mechanic. He repaired 30 trucks and 11 cabs last month. How many vehicles did he repair altogether?

**40.** Mrs. Laura used 7 gallons of fuel last week. She used 3 gallons this week. How many gallons of fuel were consumed in the two weeks?

**41.** Lizzy loves collecting small stuffed animals. She has 9 cows and 5 sheep. How many animals does she have in her collection?

**42.** A fish tank contains 5 large fish and 55 small fish. How many fish are there in the tank?

**43.** There are 15 doves and 23 crows in Shadyside Woods. How many total birds are there in Shadyside Woods?

**44.** There are 41 dogs and 10 ducks on a farm. How many animals are there on the farm?

**45.** A zoo has 7 African elephants and 9 Indian elephants. How many elephants are there in the zoo?

# CHAPTER 11: SUBTRACTION ACTIVITIES FOR KIDS MATH

1. Mr. Anderson  cleaned 66 of the 72 vans. How many are still to be cleaned?



2. A truck drove under a bridge 8 m high. There was a gap of 3 m between the top of the truck and the bridge. How many meters was the truck in height?



3. A milk van started with 30 bottles of milk. It delivered 21 bottles. How many bottles are still to be delivered?



4. Robin  has to repair 90 buses. He has repaired 3. How many more does he have to repair?

**5.** Mrs. Douglas has 8 gallons of fuel in her car. Her fuel tank has a capacity of 16 gallons. How many gallons are needed to fill the fuel tank?

**6.** Debbie has 11 teddy bears. She gives away 5 of them to her best friend. How many teddy bears does she now have?

**7.** A fish tank contains 65 fish of which 9 are stationary. How many fish in the tank are moving?

**8.** There are 91 birds in a sanctuary of which 82 are blue. How many birds are there of other colors?

**9.** A circus has 9 elephants. There are 6 elephants with tusks. How many elephants do not have tusks?

**10.** A magician starts with 11 doves and makes 6 doves vanish. How many doves remain?

**11.** Debbie bought 4 dolls for $ 4. She had $ 16 in her purse. How many dollars are left in her purse?

**12.** Cheryl has two dolls. The first doll is 22 cm tall and the second is 18 cm. What is the difference in their heights (in cm)?

**13.** Robert had 18 marbles in his school bag. He returned home with 12 marbles. How many marbles did he lose?

14. Robert arranges 16 blocks in a tall stack. Accidentally, he drops 8 blocks. How many blocks are still there in the stack?

15. Each day 66 vans are made in a toy factory. Of these, 3 are defective. How many toy vehicles are not defective?

16. Invitations were sent to 42 relatives for a family get-together. Only 40 relatives came. How many relatives did not come?

17. Arthur weighs 18 kg. His mother is 53 kg. How much more is his mother's weight (in kg)?

18. Mr. Baker will be 48 next year. His son is 35 years younger than him. How many years old is his son at present?

19. A family party has 33 adults, 9 boys, and 9 girls. How many more adults are there at the party than children?

20. Andy is 16 years old. His aunt is 46. How many years older than him is his aunt?

The table shows quiz marks out of 25 in each subject.

|         | English | Geography | Mathematics | Science |
|---------|---------|-----------|-------------|---------|
| Adam    | 9       | 19        | 22          | 5       |
| Bob     | 18      | 13        | 9           | 15      |
| Charles | 12      | 19        | 21          | 18      |

21. What is the difference between Charles'

marks in English and Science?

> [blank answer box]

**22.** How many more marks does Adam need for a perfect score in Mathematics?

> [blank answer box]

**23.** In Geography, how many more marks did Adam get than Bob?

> [blank answer box]

**24.** Find the difference between Adam's Science marks and Bob's English marks.

> [blank answer box]

**25.** The Mathematics teacher gave Charles 4 extra marks by mistake. What are his real marks?

> [blank answer box]

A mischievous monkey had collected 46 red marbles, 40 blue marbles, 14 caps, and a dozen bananas in a big bag. He decided to place 6 caps on his head and eat6 bananas. Then, while playing, he lost 16 blue marbles and 16 red marbles. He was tired and fell off to sleep. On seeing the monkey fast asleep, a fox stole the bag and ate 2 bananas.

26. How many red marbles were there in the stolen bag?

27. How many marbles were there in the stolen bag?

28. What is the maximum number of caps the fox could wear?

29. How many bananas did the fox find in the bag?

**30.** How many more bananas would the fox have to eat to finish all of them?

**31.** A board game contains 44 total coins. There are 4 blue coins, and 33 red coins. How many coins are there of other colors?

**32.** The doctors at Get-Well Hospital drank 78 cups of tea yesterday. They drank 27 cups in the morning and 32 in the afternoon. How many did they drink in the evening?

**33.** Bill borrowed 12 books from the school library. He returned 5 books yesterday and 5 books today. How many books does he still have?

**34.** Mrs. Douglas had a lovely 43-piece crockery set. Last evening, 4 cups and 5 saucers broke. How many pieces of crockery left?

**35.** Jimmy had half an hour to do his homework. He spent 5 minutes on English and 11 minutes on Science. How many minutes remain?

The distances (in km) between the following points on the simplified Road Map are :

| Home & Museum : 28 | School & Museum : 23 | Library & Museum : 19 |
|---|---|---|
| Home & Toy Shop : 22 | Pet Shop & Toy Shop : 18 | Bakery & Toy Shop : 10 |

What is the distance (in km) Steve has to travel :

**36.** from his home to school?

**37.** from the school to borrow a book at the library?

**38.** from the library to return home?

**39.** from his home to buy some cakes?

**40.** from the bakery to pick up his dog at the pet shop?

# CHAPTER 12: ARITHMETIC ACTIVITIES FOR KIDS MATH

1. There are 6 crows perched on the branch of a tree. How many feet are there on the branch?

2. A fish tank contains 7 fish of which 4 are stationary. How many fish in the tank are moving?

3. There are 4 moths with a total of 12 blue spots on their wings. If each moth has the same number of spots, how many spots on each moth?

4. There are 3 lions and 5 tigers in a circus show. How many legs are there in all?

5. A zoo has 2 African elephants and 2 Indian elephants. How many elephants are there in the zoo?

6. Grahaminvites 37 boys and 23 girls to his birthday party. How many friends did he invite?

7. There are 3 cakes. Each cake is cut into 4 pieces. How many pieces are there in all?

8. There are 16 sandwiches to be arranged equally in 2 trays. How many sandwiches will there be in each tray?

9. Dad has planned 5 games for the party. Each

game would have 3 winners. How many prizes would Dad give away?

|  |
|--|

10. Mom places 32 paper plates on the table in 8 rows. How many paper plates are there in each row?

|  |
|--|

11. Barbara bought 11 dolls. Each doll cost $ 4 .How many dollars did she spend on the dolls?

|  |
|--|

12. A board game has 15 total coins. There are equal number of coins of 5 different colors. How many coins are there of each color?

|  |
|--|

13. Robinhas 10 toy cars. How many total wheels are there on the toy cars?

**14.** Gary arranges 20 blocks in two stacks. He then arranges 29 blocks in five stacks. How many blocks did he arrange in the seven stacks?

**15.** Last Friday 49 cars were made in a toy factory. Of these, 5 were defective. How many toy vehicles were not defective?

**16.** There are 88 flowers in a bouquet. There are 4 blue flowers. How many flowers are not blue?

**17.** There are 10 flowers in a bunch. Each flower has 5 petals. How many petals are there in the bunch?

**18.** Each rose has 9 thorns. If there are a total of 36 thorns, how many roses are there?

**19.** How many bunches of 8 can be made from 72 flowers?

**20.** A florist has 10 tulips. He has 6 times as many gladioli as tulips. How many gladioli does the florist have?

**21.** Mom had given you $ 9 last week. She gives you 4 times more travel money this week. How many dollars has Mom given you over the two weeks?

**22.** The bus ticket to Squirrel Park costs 3 times

more than that to Beaver Valley. If the ticket to Beaver Valley costs $ 2 , how many dollars is the ticket to Squirrel Park?

> [                    ]

23. Squirrel Park is 3 times as far as Beaver Valley. If Squirrel Park is 15 miles from home, how many miles is Beaver Valley from home?

> [                    ]

24. There are 24 women in the bus. The women are 3 times more than the men. How many men are there in the bus?

> [                    ]

25. You had brought home 4 flowers from Squirrel Park last time. Mom wants you to bring 6 times as many this time. How many flowers will you bring?

26. Each section in a class has 8 students. If there are 4 sections, how many students are there in

the class?

---

**27.** A class picnic is estimated to cost $ 88 . If there are 11 children in the class, how many dollars should each child contribute?

---

**28.** If 18 children in a class are to be assigned 6 Science projects, how many children should work on each project?

---

**29.** The Math teacher does 6 sums everyday. After 7 days, how many sums has she done?

---

**30.** For a school day parade, there are 5 rows with 7 boys in each row and 5 rows with 8 girls in each row. How many total students are there in the parade?

The table shows quiz marks out of 25 in each subject.

|  | English | Geography | Mathematics | Science |
|---|---|---|---|---|
| Andrew | 23 | 20 | 17 | 8 |
| Brian | 20 | 12 | 17 | 6 |
| Colin | 14 | 23 | 10 | 19 |

**31.** How many marks did Colin totally obtain in Mathematics and Science?

**32.** How many more marks does Andrew need for a perfect score in Mathematics?

**33.** In Geography, how many more marks did Andrew get than Brian?

**34.** Find the difference between Andrew's Science marks and Brian's English marks.

**35.** The Mathematics teacher by mistake gave Colin 2 times his actual marks. What are his actual marks?

36. There are 3 cakes. Each cake is cut into 8 parts. Each part is further cut into 2 pieces. How many cake pieces are there in all?

**36.** The Professors at the State University drank 40 cups of tea yesterday. They drank 6 cups in the morning and 4 in the afternoon. How many did they drink in the evening?

**37.** Adam   borrowed 10 books from the school library. He returned 2 books yesterday and 4 books today. How many books does he still have?

**38.** For her new kitchen, Mrs. Diane bought a crockery set, a cutlery set and a pressure cooker. Each item cost $ 22 . How many dollars did she spend?

**39.** There are 2 paintings on each of three walls of a room. If an art gallery has 8 such rooms, how many paintings are there in its collection?

# CHAPTER 13: "AGE" WORD PROBLEMS

"Age" type word problems typically compare the ages of two people, maybe at different points in their lives. Here's an example:

In January of 2000, Sarah was eleven times as old as Bob, her son.  Sarah was seven, more than three times as old as him, in January of 2009. How old was her son in January of 2000?

You would have walked up to her kid in real life and asked him how old he was, and he would have held up three grubby fingers proudly, but that won't help you with your homework.

Here is how you would figure out his age if you had been asked the above question in your math class:

First, I will need to name things and translate English into math. Since her age was defined in Bob's, I will start with a variable for Bob's age. To make it easy for me to remember the meaning of the variable, I will pick B to stand for "Bob's age at the start, in the year 2000". Then Bob's age in 2009, being 9 years later, will be B + 9. So I have the following information:

Bob's age in 2000: B

Bob's age in 2009: B + 9

Sarah's age was defined in terms of the above expressions. In the year 2000, she was "eleven times Bob's age in the year 2000, plus one more", giving me:

Sarah's age in 2000: 11(B) + 1

Sarah's age in 2009 was also defined in terms of Bob's age in 2009. Specifically, Sarah was "three times Bob's age in 2009, plus seven more", giving me:

Sarah's age in 2009: 3(B + 9) + 7

But Sarah was also 9 years older than she had been in the year 2000, which gives me another expression for my age in 2009:

Sarah's age in 2009: [11(B) + 1] + 9

Sarah's age in 2009 was her age in 2009. This means that the two expressions for "her age in 2009" must represent the same value. And this fact allows me to create an equation (by setting the two equal-value expressions equal to each other):

$3(B + 9) + 7 = [11(B) + 1] + 9$

Solving, I get:

$3(B + 9) + 7 = [11(B) + 1] + 9$

$3B + 27 + 7 = 11B + 1 + 9$

$3B + 34 = 11B + 10$

$34 = 8B + 10$

$24 = 8B$

$3 = B$

Since I set up this equation using expressions for Sarah's age, it is tempting to think that "3 = B" stands for my age. However, this is why I picked B to stand for "Bob's age"; the variable reminds me that, no, "3 =B" stands for Bob's age, not Sarah's.

And this is exactly what the question had asked in the first place. How old was Bob in the year 2000?

Bob was 3 years old.

Note that this word problem didn't ask for the value of a variable; it asked for a person's age. So a properly-written "answer" reflects this. "B = 3" wouldn't be an ideal response.

The vital steps above were to (1) to figure out what's defined in terms of something else, (2) set up a variable for that "something else" (labeling it clearly with its definition), (3) create an expression for the first time frame, and then (4) increment the expressions by the required amount (in this case, by 9) to reflect the passage of time.

Do not try to use the same expression or variable to stand for 2 different things! Since, in the above, "B" stood for Bob's age in 2000, then "B" can not also stand for his age in 2009! Ensure that you are very clear about this when you set up your expressions, equations, and variables; write down the 2 sets of information as two distinct situations!

Currently, Nicolas is three times Andrei's age. In ten years, Nicolas will be twelve years older than Andrei. What are their ages now?

Nicolas's age is defined in terms of Andrei's age, so I'll pick a variable for Andrei's age now; say, "A." This allows me to create an expression for Nicolas' age now, which is three times that of Andrei.

Andrei' age now: A

Nicolas' age now: 3A

In 10 years, they will be ten years older, so I will add ten to each of the above for their later ages.

Andrei's age later: A + 10

Nicolas' age later: 3A + 10

But I'm also given that, in ten years, Nicolas will be 12 years older than Andrei. So I can create another expression for Nicolas' age in 10 years; namely, I will take the expression for Andrei's age in 10 years and add 12 to that.

Nicolas' age later: [A + 10] + 12

Since Nicolas' future age will equal his future age, I can take these 2 expressions for his future age, set them equal by creating an equation, and solve the variable's value.

3A + 10 = [A + 10] + 12

3A + 10 = A + 22

2A + 10 = 22

2A = 12

A = 6

Okay, I have found the value of the variable. However, looking back at the original question, I see that they want to know two people's current ages. The variable stands for the age of the younger of the two. Since the older is three times this age, then the older is eighteen years old. So my clearly-stated answer is:

Andrei is 6 years old.

Nicolas is 18 years old.

One-half of Richard's age 2 years from now plus one-third of his age three years ago is twenty years. How old is she now?

This problem refers to Richard's age 2 years into the future and 3 years back in the past. Unlike most "age" word problems, this exercise is not comparing 2 different people's ages at the same time, but instead the same person's ages at different points in time.

They ask for Richard's age now, so I will pick a variable to stand for this unknown; say, R. Then I will increment this variable in order to create expressions for "2 years ago" and "2 years from now".

age now: R

age two years from now: R + 2

age three years ago: R − 3

Now I need to create expressions, using the above, which will stand for certain fractions of these ages:

½ of age 2 years from now: \small{ \dfrac{1}{2} \left(R + 2\right) }21    (R+2)

\small{ \frac{1}{3} }31    of age 3 years ago: \small{ \dfrac{1}{3} \left(R - 3\right) }31    (R−3)

The sum of these 2 expressions is given as being "20", so I will add the two expressions, set their sum equal to twenty, and solve for the variable:

\small{ \frac{1}{2} (R + 2) + \frac{1}{3} (R - 3) = 20 }21    (R+2)+31    (R−3)=20

\small{ \frac{1}{2} R + 1 + \frac{1}{3} R - 1 = 20 }21    R+1+31    R−1=20

\small{ \frac{1}{2} R + \frac{1}{3} R = 20 }21    R+31    R=20

\small{ 3R + 2R = 120 }3R+2R=120

\small{ 5R = 120 }5R=120

\small{ R = 24 }R=24

So I have found the value of the variable. Now I will go back and check my definition of that variable (so I see that it stands for Richard's current age), and I will check for what the exercise actually asked me to find (which was Richard's current age). So my answer is:

Richard is 24 years old.

Note: remember that by plugging the answer back into the original problem, you can always check your answer to any "solving" exercise.

In the above exercise, if Richard is now 24, then in two years, he would be 26, half of which is 13; three years ago, she would have been 21, one-third of which is 7.

Adding, I get 13 7=

20, so my solution "checks."

In 3 more years, Sophia's grandmother will be six times as old as Sophia was last year. When Sophia's present age is added to his grandmother's present age, the total is 68. How old is each one now?

The grandmother's age is defined in terms of Sophia's age, so I will pick a variable to stand for

Sophia's age. Since they are asking me for current ages, my variable will stand for Sophia's current age.

Sophia's age now: s

Now I will use this variable to create expressions for the various items listed in the exercise.

Sophia's age last year: s – 1

six times Sophia's age last year: 6(s – 1)

Sophia's grandmother's age will, in another 3 years, be 6 times what Sophia's age was last year. This means that his grandmother is currently 3 years less than 6 times Sophia's age from last year, so:

grandmother's age now: 6(s – 1) – 3

Summing the expressions for the two current ages and solving, I get:

$(s) + [6(s – 1) – 3] = 68$

$s + [6s – 6 – 3] = 68$

$s + [6s – 9] = 68$

$7s – 9 = 68$

$7s = 77$

s = 11

Looking back, I see that this variable stands for Sophia's current age, which is 11. But the exercise asks me for the current ages of both of them, so:

Last year, Sophia would have been 10. In three more years, his grandmother will be six times ten or sixty. So his grandmother must currently be 60 − 3 = 57.

Sophia is currently 11.

His grandmother is currently 57.

A grammarian called Metrodorus collected "epigrams" in fifth-century Greece, which were usually brief poems that had been inscribed somewhere, such as on someone's tomb. He published an anthology of mathematical puzzlers, each in the form of a poem.

One of these poems relates to the life, and the age at death, of a 3rd-century mathematician named Diophantus, who lived in Alexandria, Egypt (but was presumably of Greek heritage). A groundbreaking collection of books called "Arithmetica" was written by Diophantus and is known by many as "the father of algebra."

Despite all the truly modern mathematics that Diophantus did (including developing the area of study that would later come to be called "Diophantine equations"), most algebra students know him only from the Metrodorus poem in numerous English translations. To find out how long Diophantus lived, students are supposed to dissect the puzzler. Here's how it works:

"Here lies Diophantus," the wonder behold...

Through art algebraic, the stone tells how old:

"God gave him his boyhood one-sixth of his life,

One-twelfth more as a youth while whiskers grew rife;

And then yet one-seventh ere marriage began;

In five years, there came a bouncing new son.

Alas, this dear child of master and sage,

He attained only half of his father's full age.

When chill fate took him — an event full of tears —

Heartbroken, his father lived just four more years."

How long did Diophantus live?

My first assignment is to "translate" the poetry into realistic terms from the headstone.

Some guesses and assumptions would have to be made by anyone solving this puzzler; here is a set that works out at the end:

I'm going to assume that "boyhood" is pre-adolescent childhood, particularly because "whiskers" are mentioned later.

So, in this period, he spent one-sixth of his life.

"Youth while whiskers grew" could stand for pubescence (i.e., in teen years, into young adulthood); in this time, he spent one-twelfth of his life.

"Ere marriage began" may denote "bachelorhood" or "unmarried adulthood"; in this period, he spent one-seventh of his life.

There were five years between his wedding and the time his first child was born.

Tragically, this child died young, living just half as long as his father would eventually; looking the other way, half of Diophantus' life was spent while his child was alive.

· Diophantus died 4 years after his child was buried.

First thing first.

I'm supposed to find out the age of Diophantus, so I'll take the variable d for the age of Diophantus at death.

Working with this variable, I can then create expressions for each of the listed periods in Diophantus's life.

childhood: \small{ }d/6

adolescence: d/12

bachelorhood: d/7

childless marriage: 5

age of child at death: d/2

life after child's death: 4

His whole life had been divided into intervals which, when added together, give the sum of his life. So I'll add the lengths of those periods, set their sum equal to his (as-yet unknown) total age, and solve:

.d/6 + d/12 + d/7 + 5 + d/2 + 4 = d

( 25/28 )d + 9 = d

9 = d – ( 25/28 )d

9 = ( 3/28 )d

84 = d

Diophantus lived to be 84 years old.

You can plug "84" into the original problem to check the answer if you like. If he lived to be 84, then one-twelfth of his life is 7 years (so he'd be 21, and he certainly should have a beard by this age), one-sixth of his life is 14 years, one-seventh of his life is 12 years (so he didn't marry until he was 33 years old), his child was born when he was 38, the boy died at 42 (when Diophantus was 80), and then Diophantus died four years later.

# CHAPTER 14: 3<sup>RD</sup> GRADE MATHS WORD PROBLEMS!

Are you looking for engaging 3rd-grade math word problems with answers to add to your upcoming lesson plans? The following collection of free 3rd-grade math word problems worksheets cover topics including addition, subtraction, multiplication, division, and measurement.

These free 3rd-grade math word problem worksheets can be shared at home or in the classroom, and they are great for warm-ups and cool-downs, transitions, extra practice, homework, and credit assignments.

Enjoy!

Word Problems: Subtraction

Directions | Carefully read each question, identify the key information, show all of your work, and circle your final answer!

1. Leo has 33 pieces of candy leftover from Halloween. If he gives 14 pieces of candy away to his friends, how many pieces of candy does he have left?

2. Anne Marie rides her bike to school every day. The bike ride from her house to her school takes her 41 minutes. If she has already been biking for 17 minutes, how much longer does she have to ride before she arrives at school?

3. Lisa is inviting people to her birthday party. She gets 50 invitations made to share with her friends. She starts by handing out 29 invitations to her friends in her neighborhood and plans to hand out the rest at school. How many invitations does she have left to hand out at school?

4. Caroline baked 93 cookies to sell at her bakery. She plans on taking home whatever cookies she doesn't sell. If she sold 77 cookies, how many cookies will she be taking home?

5. A bottle contains 22 ounces of soda. If Joey pours 10 ounces into a cup and drinks it all and the pours 5 more ounces into a cup and drinks all of that too, how many ounces of soda are left in the bottle?

6. A movie theatre has 90 total seats. If 39 seats are currently taken by people with movie tickets, how many empty seats are still available?

Word Problems: Addition

Directions | Carefully read each question, identify the key information, show all of your work, and circle your final answer!

7. Before going out trick-or-treating on Halloween night, Geoff spent 10 minutes putting on his costume, Lilly spent 8 minutes putting on her costume, and Trish spent 20 minutes putting on her costume. How much total time did it take them to put on their costumes?

8. On Halloween night, Chris went trick-or-treating at 12 houses. If Luigi visited 9 more houses than Chris did, how many houses did Luigi visit?

9. After a long night of trick-or-treating, Calvin counted his candy and saw that he had 25 chocolate candies, 15 gummy candies, and 30 hard candies. How many candies does Calvin have in total?

10. Tulsi, Carley, and Roxanne decide to combine all of their Halloween candy together. Tulsi has 65 pieces of candy, Carley has 25 pieces of candy, and Roxanne has 35 pieces of candy. How much candy do they have in total?

11. On Halloween night, Nora spent 90 minutes trick-or-treating, Brent spent 60 minutes trick-or-treating, Arnold spent 75 minutes trick-or-treating, and Camille spent 25 minutes trick-or-treating. Which pair spent more total time trick-or-treating:

Nora and Camille OR Brent and Arnold?

# CHAPTER 15: FAILING IN MATH

Often before, I spoke about the learning challenges faced today by students. Two big factors contributing to unmotivated math students are the school curriculum's reformation and the standard of instruction. These, however, are extrinsic, uncontrollable concerns. I would also like to focus more on the intrinsic variables so that parents and students can do anything to boost their math.

1. Math Scare Index Evaluation: (check from 1 to 5 where 1 = strongly disagrees and five = strongly agrees)

1. I'm concerned that my math report card is smaller than the class average.

2. My math class at school doesn't like me.

3. At school, I don't know how to ask math questions.

4. I think that I'm an illiterate mathematician.

5. I need someone to give me tutoring and extra support.

6. I fear that I may lose my competitive edge in my profession due to my lack of math skills.

7. Just one type of intellect is arithmetic. I still have other kinds of intellect, even though I am not good at it.

8. With numbers, I am not fine.

9. Word questions frighten and bother me all the time.

10. In my real life, I don't know how to apply algebra.

Attach your ratings in total.

If you have: 10-18: You're very positive, and you're at the top of the math class.

19-26: To be at the top of the class, you can quickly catch up.

27-34: You are not on your own. Students are just like you. Work a little more, and you're going to graduate.

35-42: You don't have much faith in math, and you need extra support.

43-50: You have to contact a competent consultant to seek help immediately.

2. You must figure out exactly what kind of challenges they face after assessing to find out where the child stands in terms of math. Several questions often posed by parents are below.

a. How come my children still get good grades on their homework; however, they miss their tests? We have to decide if they grasp the idea of homework exercises to address this question. Some children want to ask for the solution while completing their homework without knowing how to get to it. To assist them with their homework, certain children need tutors, but logical reasoning is far more important and useful than finding the correct answer.

b. Will buying workout books for my child help?

It can also help to do certain drills, but children also become machines, doing the same boring tasks without thought. Some children are much worse and memorize the key to the answer. Exercise books are usually for more mature students who choose to perform more complex activities.

c. How do I know whether my child understands or pretends to grasp the concept?

Whenever teachers ask students whether or not they understand, most respond with 'yes.' But, later on, when teachers use the same term to offer a similar exercise, most students cannot respond. Each teacher is assigned to teach in a traditional classroom environment to so many students with different IQ levels of comprehension. It is, however, nearly difficult for a teacher to diagnose a student's problems. Fortunately, parents often follow their elementary children with their homework to figure out precisely where the issue is. Sadly, this is rarely the case with children in high school.

d. My baby was a math loser at a young age. What am I capable of doing?

Failure is part of the experience of living. Success is hard to come by without suffering disappointment. I give parents a chance to discuss and analyze the challenges faced by their children in this essay (I).

When small children display suspicious behavior, it is fair to assume a need for clinical consultation.

To measure their kids for early warning, one may use the Clancy Behavior Scale or ADHD test.

However, occasionally, it may just be a false warning. I've experienced a few cases in the past. I talked to a couple of parents who told me that they had learning disabilities and wanted specialist consultants for their two daughters, aged seven and nine. I was able to understand the situation better after teaching them math for a few years. They made considerable improvement, retaining above-average marks and responding interactively to others as normal. I also had a regular friendship with the kids and their guardians. Due to cultural and language differences in the classroom, immigrant children are very frequently misunderstood for learning disabilities. These children need more care and affection.

Family life is crucial: frequent quarreling between parents in the household will lead to children's emotional dysfunction. In exchange, this can stall their progression in schooling. Parents have a responsibility to have a caring and disciplined atmosphere at home so that their children can learn. When children can learn but do not learn well, the mistake will likely be due to the teachers' educational level.

When he apologized to the students who failed in his class, I was moved by a university professor. Forty percent of the students in the class have refused to take a midterm test before. He apologized to them and said that it was not good enough for his reasons and teaching ability. Kids are like blank sheets of paper, waiting for teachers to have quality guidance and inspiration. I also advise parents in front of their kids that we're the ones to blame if school grades don't change. The only prerequisite is that they cooperate with us entirely.

One in ten students in a private school across Canada, but in Quebec, the figure leaps to 2.9:10, nearly tripling the norm. This broad gap indicates that parents value teachers in private schools even more than teachers of public schools. When some students showed us some quality class lectures and assignments, I showed respect and gratitude to many good teachers. Sadly, some educators can't answer more challenging questions or are reluctant to answer them. They either tell the students that they will come to them later and then fully forget about it, or they tell the students that since they are so easy, they should be able to answer the problems, thereby disguising their incapacity.

Parents, teachers, a positive quote, a movie, or a book need and deserve to be enlightened by every infant. A very good example is the very famous inventor, Thomas Edison.

## Final Thoughts about Math Word Problems

You will likely get the most out of this resource by using the problems as templates, slightly modifying them by applying the above tips. In doing so, they will be more relevant to -- and engaging for -- your students. Regardless, having enough curriculum aligned math word problems at your fingertips should help you deliver skill-building difficulties and thought-provoking assessments. The result? A greater understanding of how your students process content and show understanding, informing your ongoing teaching approach.

# CHAPTER 16: ANSWER TO QUESTIONS

## MATH WORD PROBLEMS, CATEGORIZED BY SKILL

### ADDITION

1.  3 shots
2.  10 pieces of gum
3.  84 pieces of gum
4.  187 Chairs
5.  26074 trading cards
6.  590 biscuits
7.  5 books
8.  279 candies
9.  956 students
10. 781 points
11. $705
12. 281 wild animals
13. 11649 DVDs
14. 732 calls
15. 2590 participants
16. 2700m
17. 4015 pages
18. 6727 birds
19. 100934 copies
20. 648300 bolts

**21.** 9565687

**22.** 564331 books

## SUBTRACTION

**23.** 229 healthy pets

**24.** 92 eggs

**25.** 280 girls

**26.** 109 minutes

**27.** 154 pages

**28.** 5519 video DVD

**29.** $4001

**30.** 254 points

**31.** 2734 females

**32.** 90001

**33.** 238857 miles

**34.** $15096

**35.** $205857

**36.** 2 pizzas

**37.** 4 stickers

**38.** 66 pieces of gum

**39.** 40 points

**40.** 755 ants

**41.** 8201 trading cards

**42.** 107 candies

**43.** 33 crayons

## MULTIPLICATION

44. 32 brownies
45. 300 seats
46. 80 bricks
47. 250000 sweatshirts
48. $480
49. 21 batches of cupcakes
50. 36 students
51. 63 cookies
52. $40
53. 120 baseball cards
54. 99 seats

## DIVISION

55. 2 pieces of candy
56. 300 pieces
57. 10 rides
58. $2.5 for 1 tennis ball and $5 for 1 pack
59. 5 cookies
60. 3 hours
61. 63 cookies
62. $40
63. 25 watermelons
64. 4 times

## MEASUREMENT

65. 9 inches long

**66.** 36cm

**67.** 6 feet tall

**68.** 2 feet long

**69.** 120 inches long

**70.** 70 cm long

## MATH WORD PROBLEMS FOR THIRD GRADERS

| Tree | Height (m) |
|---|---|
| Australian Mountain Ash | 100 |
| Coast Douglas Fir | 99 |
| Coast Redwood | 116 |
| Giant Sequoia | 95 |
| Manna Gum | 89 |
| Sitka Spruce | 97 |
| Tasmanian Blue Gum | 91 |

1) Use the data below to complete the missing information in the table.

- The Sitka Spruce is 8m taller than the Manna Gum tree.

- The Giant Sequoia is 21m shorter than the Coast Redwood.

- The Manna Gum is 11m shorter than the Australian Mountain Ash.

2) Put the trees in order of height, from 1 to 7, with 1 being the shortest and 7 being the tallest.

3) How much taller is the Coast Redwood than the Sitka Spruce? 19m

4) How much shorter is the Manna Gum than the Coast Redwood? 27m

5) Tyger climbs halfway up a tree. He is 45½m off the ground. Which tree has he climbed? Tasmanian Blue Gum

6) The height of an mature oak tree is about 21m. Tyger says "The Coast Redwood is taller than 5 oak trees together." Is he correct?

5 x 21 = 105m. Coast Redwood is 116m. He is correct.

Tallest Light houses

|  | Height (ft) | Order ( |
|---|---|---|
|  | 271 | 4 |
|  | 436 | 1 |
| Genoa | 253 | 5 |
| ial Monument | 352 | 2 |
| eville | 247 | 6 |
| arine Tower | 332 | 3 |

1. Use these facts to complete the table above:

- The Lighthouse of Genoa is 18ft lower than the Ile Vierge.

- The Jeddah Light is 84ft higher than the Perry Memorial Monument.

- The Yokohama Marine Tower is 61ft higher than the Ile Vierge.

2. Fill in the order of height from 1 to 6, with 1 being the tallest.

3. How much taller is the Perry Memorial Monument than the Phare de Gatteville? 105ft

4. How much shorter is the Ile Vierge than the Jeddah Light? 165ft

5. Tyger says "The Jeddah Light is more than double the height of the shortest tower." Is he correct? 247 x 2 = 494ft. Jeddah = 436ft. He is wrong!

6. Which tower is closest to 300ft in height? Ile Vierge (29ft away).

7. Tyger says "If you put three Yokohama towers on top of each other, it would make about 1000ft." Is he correct? 332 x 3 = 996ft. He is correct.

**Members of the cat family**

| Name | Average Weight (kg) |
|------|---------------------|

| | |
|---|---|
| Cheetah | 60 |
| Lynx | 26 |
| Lion | 190 |
| Cougar | 73 |
| Leopard | 67 |
| Tiger | 227 |

1) Use the information below to complete the information in the table:

- The cheetah is 7kg lighter than a leopard.

- The tiger can run 13kph faster than a lynx.

- The tiger is 37kg heavier than a lion.

2) Put the animals in order of weight, from lightest to heaviest.

 Lynx   Cheetah   Leopard   Cougar   Lion   Tiger

3) How much heavier is a cougar than a lynx? 47 kg

4) How much faster is a cheetah than a leopard? 63 kph

5) Tyger says "The cheetah is more than twice as fast as a leopard." Is he right? Leopard is 58kph. Double 58 is 116kph. Cheetah is 121kph. So he is correct.

6) Tyger says "A lion is a faster and heavier animal than a tiger." Is he right? A lion is faster than a tiger but not as heavy so he is wrong.

7) Tyger says "A cougar would be heavier than 3 lynxes." Is he right? Cougar is 73kg. Lynx is 26kg. 3 Lynxes is 26 x 3 = 78kg. He is wrong.

Tallest buildings throughout history.

| Name of building | Year | Where |
|---|---|---|
| Great Pyramid of Giza | 2570 BC | Egypt |
| Lincoln Cathedral | 1311 | England |
| Washington Monument | 1884 | US |
| Eiffel Tower | 1889 | France |
| Chrysler Building | 1930 | US |
| Empire State Building | 1931 | US |

| | | |
|---|---|---|
| Ostankino Tower | 1967 | Russi |
| CN Tower | 1975 | Car |
| Burj Khalifa | 2007 | Dubа |

1) Use the information below to complete the missing data in the table.

2) The Eiffel Tower was built 5 years after the Washington Monument.

3) Washington Monument is 29ft taller than Lincoln Cathedral.

4) The Great Pyramid was 46ft lower than Lincoln Cathedral.

5) Ostankino Tower was built 36 years after the Empire State Building.

6) The CN Tower is 52ft taller than the Ostankino Tower and was built 45 years after the Chrysler Building.

7) Round all the heights to the nearest 10ft, filling in the column.

8) How much taller is the Eiffel Tower than the Washington Monument?

430 ft

4) Tyger says "The Burj Khalifa is taller than the Chrysler Building and the
Empire State Building put together." Is he correct?

Burj Khalifa = 2723ft Chrysler + Empire = 1046 +

1250 = 1296 ft. He is correct.

## WORD PROBLEM YEAR THREE

1. Answer: 229
2. Answer: 82
3. Answer: 32
4. Answer: Leo = 500ml, Bill = 300ml
5. Answer: James by 11p.

## WORD PROBLEM YEAR FOUR

1. Answer: 150
2. Answer: 108m
3. Answer: 30cm2

## WORD PROBLEM YEAR FIVE

1. Answer: 9 and 2/6 or 9 and 1/3
2. Answer: 200

# WORD PROBLEM YEAR 6

1. Answer: -5Oc
2. Answer: 311
3. Answer: 0.25 and 0.75
4. Answer: 20 pots
5. Answer: 864m3

# 3<sup>RD</sup> GRADE MATHS WORD PROBLEMS!

## ANSWERS

1. 19 candies
2. 24 minutes
3. 21 invitations
4. 16 cookies
5. 7 ounces
6. 51 seats
7. 38 minutes
8. 21 houses
9. 70 candies
10. 125 candies

11. Nora and Camille: 115 minutes, Brent and Arnold: 135 minutes (Brent and Arnold spent the most time trick-or-treating)

# ADDITION ACTIVITIES FOR KIDS

1. 13
2. 49
3. 57
4. 10
5. 8
6. 39
7. 78
8. 94
9. 78
10. 11
11. 52
12. 45
13. 69
14. 120
15. 31
16. 61
17. 60
18. 22
19. 41
20. 19
21. 30

**22.** 43

**23.** 16

**24.** 59

**25.** 82

**26.** 62

**27.** 72

**28.** 57

**29.** 40

**30.** 12

**31.** 75

**32.** 11

**33.** 61

**34.** 46

**35.** 66

**36.** 71

**37.** 50

**38.** 47

**39.** 41

**40.** 10

**41.** 14

**42. 60**

**43. 38**

**44. 51**

**45. 16**

# SUBTRACTION ACTIVITIES FOR KIDS

1. 6
2. 5
3. 9
4. 87
5. 8
6. 6
7. 56
8. 9
9. 3
10. 5
11. 12
12. 4
13. 6
14. 8
15. 63
16. 2
17. 35
18. 12
19. 15
20. 30
21. 6
22. 3
23. 6
24. 13
25. 17
26. 30
27. 54
28. 8
29. 6
30. 4

31. 7

32. 19

33. 2

34. 34

35. 14

36. 5

37. 4

38. 9

39. 12

40. 8

# ARITHMETIC ACTIVITIES FOR KIDS

1. 12

2. 3

3. 3

4. 32

5. 4

6. 60

7. 12

8. 8

9. 15

10. 4

11. 44

12. 3

13. 40

14. 49

**15.** 44

**16.** 84

**17.** 50

**18.** 4

**19.** 9

**20.** 60

**21.** 36

**22.** 6

**23.** 45

**24.** 8

**25.** 24

**26.** 32

**27.** 8

**28.** 3

**29.** 42

**30.** 75

**31.** 29

**32.** 8

**33.** 12

**34.** 5

**35.** 48

**36.** 30

**37.** 4

**38.** 66

**39.** 48

Lightning Source UK Ltd.
Milton Keynes UK
UKHW022249210421
382399UK00003B/236

9 781802 662245